Discerning Charisms:

A workbook for navigating the discernment process

The Catherine of Siena Institute
PO Box 26440
Colorado Springs, Colorado 80936

(719) 219-0056 Seattle area
(888) 878-6789 toll free U.S.
info@siena.org e-mail
www.siena.org

Introduction

How to use this workbook

Welcome to the further adventures of the discernment process! This workbook is intended to deepen the knowledge you gained from the *Called & Gifted Workshop*, whether you experienced it by video, audiotape, or through the Catherine of Siena Institute's weekend seminar. As such, there are several prerequisites to satisfy if this workbook is to be maximally beneficial:

1. You've attended or listened to the full Workshop and have completed the *Catholic Spiritual Gifts Inventory*
2. You truly intend to take action in your discernment, not just read or think about the spiritual gifts at work in your life
3. You're willing to invest at least two hours a week deliberately experimenting with a charism
4. You're willing to involve other people in your discernment efforts

If you answer "no" to any of these, this book may not prove helpful to you at this time. If you haven't experienced the Workshop, this material will be out of context—context you need in order to discern successfully. If this describes you, contact the Catherine of Siena Institute for basic Workshop materials needed. It will be worth the effort. The Institute also offers additional discernment resources. Taken together, they will guide you through the exciting journey of discovering how God has called and gifted you, an approach to Christ of singular effectiveness for lay people living their faith in the world.

The whole program of this workbook rests upon the basic Christian understanding of reality:

- ❑ God is a deeply loving Creator who is infinitely beyond us in wisdom, mercy, goodness and power, yet who united himself with humanity in Jesus Christ so that we may rise free and whole from all that twists, binds and destroys us.
- ❑ Human beings are not simply recipients of God's action, but also collaborators with him.[1] We are made for love and freedom and can indeed attain them with the help of God's grace.[2]
- ❑ God is at work in Creation *now*, healing and restoring all things, and he has chosen to carry out this work through the free assent and cooperation of men and women.[3]

This understanding is part of the good news revealed in Jesus Christ who is God become a human being.

---

[1] In Christian understanding, God is a divine person and Jesus taught that God is a passionately loving Father to us. To honor the deeply loving and fully personal nature of God, Christians have used the masculine personal pronoun when speaking of God while recognizing that God is certainly not exclusively masculine but the source of both femaleness and maleness since both women and men are made in God's image.

[2] Grace is the supernatural, free, and unearned gift of God that enables human beings to reach the eternal, perfect happiness with God for which they were created.

[3] The charisms are given to accomplish this collaboration.

The program also stands firmly on a deep respect for the entire 2000-year apostolic tradition that is found in the Catholic Church. We believe that Christ founded the Church to be the first means of his continuing presence in our world. In her totality, the Church—despite the failures of her individual members—presents the clearest sign and truest agent of Christ's presence and redeeming love in the world. This totality includes her worship, her prayer, the lives of the saints, and the teaching of Scripture and Tradition. We also believe these spiritual riches are the rightful inheritance of *every* human being, the surest guide to a fully human and meaningful life, and the shortest route to ultimate happiness thereafter.

If you do not share our understanding, that's okay. Discernment is all about testing things for yourself and holding on to what is good. Some who are drawn to the *Called & Gifted Workshop* are not Catholic, or even Christian for that matter. But that's okay. The fundamental question is: **Are you seeking to understand and do God's will, and to be an instrument of his love for others?** If you can answer yes, that's enough to begin discerning your gifts.

However, the benefits of full communion with the Church are real. The Holy Spirit normally empowers an individual with grace and initially bestows the charisms through the sacraments of Baptism and Confirmation.[4] Moreover, the charisms themselves develop most successfully within the larger context of the whole faith, supported by the sacraments–the prime vehicles of God's transforming love and the main way he teaches our hearts.

If you are Protestant, Anglican, or Orthodox, welcome! This material is firmly based on Scripture. We hope you'll find the references throughout, and those listed for each charism in the *Spiritual Gifts Resource Guide,* helpful and stimulating. We would like to add that we come across many erroneous ideas about the Catholic Church floating around our culture. We provide a list of books and other resources (see page 74) that we believe convey an accurate and informative picture of Catholic belief and practice for you to consult if you are curious.

If you're not Christian, we're happy to have the chance to introduce you to one of the deepest reservoirs of wisdom and well-traveled paths to effective decision-making, fulfillment and true happiness known to humankind. Although we will be appealing to the common language and experience of Christians, the touch of God's finger on the human heart is universal. We hope, furthermore, that you, too, will benefit from the wealth of practical knowledge the Church has conserved and cultivated for two millennia.

Whatever your background, your desire to know what God wants from you and your wish to love and serve others form our common starting point. As for the other requirements for using this workbook successfully, taking action and seeking objective feedback from other people are essential. Reading and thinking about charisms can help you recognize their traits, but constitutes only a tiny fraction of the discernment process. You have to act! The true work of discernment lies in exploring the unique shape a charism takes in your hands—and learning to follow the guidance the Holy Spirit provides through it. That kind of discernment is impossible without action. As the saying goes, God can't steer a parked car. The goal of this workbook is to guide you into that active exploration process.

---

[4] See the article on these sacraments on page 72

You can't discern in a vacuum

To use this workbook effectively, you must be willing and able to admit others into your discernment process. That primarily means two things: you will experiment with a charism by putting it to use to serve others, and you will seek out—and submit to—other people's experience of your gifts. This can be one of the most challenging aspects of charism discernment. It involves a bit of risk-taking and humility we're not necessarily used to. Ideally, you're starting this process with a small group of other people with the same desire. This workbook is primarily designed for an individual discerning with a small group.

The advantages of a small-group setting are many. First, it reduces the feeling of risk; you're all in the adventure together. It also gives you a forum to voice your questions, fears and frustrations, and a place to share your discoveries. You have the benefit of other people's ideas as you're trying to come up with good ways to experiment with a particular charism, and you benefit from their feedback, as well. Fellow discerners can tell you what they receive through you—an invaluable tool for discernment. Best of all, sharing in others' discernment efforts keeps you from getting too caught up in your own hopes and fears about yourself, one of the pitfalls of this process!

You can establish a discernment group through the Siena Institute's *Extended Discernment Program*, or simply use this workbook with a self-organized small group. It could be a group of friends or coworkers, a prayer group, a Cursillo, Marriage Encounter, or Knights of Columbus group, or a seasonal faith-sharing group such as those that many parishes set up during Lent. We only ask that the whole group first have participated in the *Called & Gifted Workshop*, either live or by using the audio or video version designed for this purpose. Contact the Institute for these resources, and for facilitators' materials and training.

What to do if you're on your own

You can use this workbook effectively, however, even if you are working without a group of fellow discerners. You will need to make sure you explore a gift in *concrete ways* that allow you to get *real feedback* from those who may receive the benefits of the charism. You want to gather objective information on what actually happens when you exercise a potential gift, so you aren't operating solely on how you felt while using it. We'll look at this issue in depth in the next section.

How this workbook is organized

This book is organized to follow the discernment process over time *as you experiment* with a particular charism, whether alone or with a group. Each section or chapter corresponds to one discernment "session." Each session begins with some helpful information about the discernment process and a guided reflection exercise to do on your own. If you're part of a group, you'll do the reading in advance, and then discuss your responses together. You will want to read the whole chapter through before meeting with your discernment group.

Part of the art of discernment is learning to listen to the urge to do what is good moment by moment, to cultivate an open and responsive ear to God's voice. Try and

5

practice this in the discernment process itself. Take this information and reflection material at your own pace, whatever seems best to you. Mainly for the sake of small groups, we have designed the workbook around a six-week period, with two weeks spent on each discernment session. We have found, through the Siena Institute's *Extended Discernment Program*, that small discernment groups work best when they meet every other week. This gives people time to experiment, as well as time to absorb their discoveries.

Six weeks spent with this workbook will not be enough time for most people to fully discern their charisms or gain a clear sense of their unique vocation. However, it should be enough time to learn the basics about discernment and charisms, to gain some significant knowledge about yourself and your relationship with God (if you're truly willing), and to experience what discernment "feels" like. Our goal is that you will have at least one experience of what it's like to use a charism.

To get the most from this workbook

1. Read the material for the session

2. Take time to do the On Your Own reflection

3. Meet with group to share

4. Experiment

Getting Started

What is 'discernment'?

At rock bottom, discernment is the practice of distinguishing the voice of God from among the many competing urgings that vie for our attention. The word "discern" originally meant "to cut away." Discernment, therefore, is the fundamental art of separating the tangled motivations that pull like invisible threads at our hearts, cutting away all but those that come from the Lord. As such, it is a basic skill necessary for all Christians. Looking at it from another angle, it is the ability to uncover satisfying answers to humanity's two perennial questions: "Who am I?," and, "Why am I here?" Discernment is a listening skill closely connected to prayer, which applies to our whole Christian life and not just to identifying our charisms.

> **Discernment is the practice of distinguishing God's voice, the promptings of Love, from:**
> - The tug of our unmet needs and fears
> - The urges of personal compulsions, such as guilt, control, etc.
> - The legitimate attractions and pleasures of created goods
> - The weight of our own rationalizations
> - The urge to do-it-yourself

The *Called & Gifted Program,* and this workbook in particular, however, concentrate on discerning *charisms.* When you discern a charism, you look at your motivations and past experience, and cut away everything except the ways you seem to be called and especially effective in serving others. You focus on these special areas to determine how God is using you as an instrument of his peace, love and providence for others. Then you take action in this area, watching for confirming results. Charisms are only one way the voice of God guides us, a very distinct, identifiable way. Such distinctness makes focusing on them an excellent way to begin the critical life task of discerning God's call. Your charisms are real clues to who you are created to be and what you are here to do!

> *"All of us have been called, the fact that you have been given a gift may constitute a call."*
>
> — *Mother Teresa of Calcutta*

The Three Signs of a Charism

A charism is a spiritual gift granted by the Holy Spirit that gives a Christian special empowerment to bring God's redeeming love into the world. Whether we're talking about the soothing gift of Mercy or the fiery gift of Prophecy, charisms always bear certain marks that allow us to recognize them with confidence as gifts of the Holy Spirit. There are three basic signs to look for. Learn them now, for we shall refer to them often.

1. **An unmistakable *inner* experience of peace, energy and joy when you're using the gift**
2. **Unusually effective and successful results in what you're trying to accomplish**
3. **Other people's direct or indirect recognition of the gift's presence**

When you can honestly say that your inner experience, actual results, and others' responses all point to a specific gift, *you can move forward under the assumption that you've discerned the presence of a charism.* On the other hand, if any of these three remains missing after you've thoroughly experimented with the gift over a significant period of

7

time, you can rest confidently that God is not calling you in that way. These steps sum up the discernment process in a nutshell, which can make it sound deceptively quick and easy. It's not. But although neither quick nor easy, the process is rational and reliable.

> *Charisms are ways God regularly uses us as channels of his loving provision for others and to build up and further the work of the Church.*

Characteristics of Charisms

Looking more closely, we can discover four characteristics of charisms that lie behind the three signs we've just discussed. Charisms are *supernatural, focused outward, received*, and *lasting*.

Supernatural Results: Charisms are a grace of God

A major reason why inner experience and objective results are vital indicators of a charism is that the spiritual gifts are *numinous*—not of this world but of the divine. They are a form of grace. Both your experience of them and their impact on the world lie beyond the ordinary, beyond the merely human: their effects are quite literally *super*-natural. These are gifts God offers us so we may collaborate in *his* loving purposes, which means that every charism is meant to achieve an end that is above and beyond our natural abilities. If you have a charism of Teaching for example, people learn as if God himself were instructing…because *he is*. That's why a spiritual gift, unlike a human talent, cannot be used for evil. It's also why you can expect amazing results when a charism is fully engaged. In fact, you will very likely be as surprised as everyone else at how well things turn out! Not only because the impact exceeds your expectations, but because the results may not be those *you* were aiming for. [5]

From the inside, your experience of the gift-in-action will also be better than expected. That sense of being energized, empowered and joyful will feel good. Pleasurable, yes, but even more: it will feel *Good*—as in *right*—just, appropriate, even beautiful. Acting through charisms can feel deeply satisfying in a way you won't experience otherwise. This characteristic makes perfect sense when you remember that charisms are supernatural. As St. Paul says, "What the Spirit brings is very different."[6] Grace is flowing through you, and we know that peace, joy and love, which we often experience as the energy to respond and act[7], are fruits of grace.

Focused outward: Gifts given to be given away

We spoke above of the need to confirm our inner experience and objective success with a third sign, i.e., others' responses. This need follows from another key characteristic of charisms: they are always focused *outward. We* are not the main beneficiaries. Though it is we who receive the supernatural empowerment, charisms are meant for others, not us. This outward focus is what allows us to distinguish charisms from both natural talents and certain other encounters with grace.

---

[5] This also extends to your vocation. The work of love God has specially equipped you for is one that exceeds your natural abilities, it's greater than anything you could possibly accomplish on your own.
[6] *Galatians 5:22*
[7] St. Teresa of Avila says that love does not consist in beautiful feelings but in a great and efficacious desire to do the will of God. *Interior Castle*, Fourth Mansions, Chapter 1.

8

Charisms versus natural talents

Natural talents can be hard to discern from Spirit-endowed gifts (particularly the creative charisms like Craftsmanship, Music, and Writing). Both natural abilities and supernatural charisms are vital to understanding and fulfilling our vocation. They work together. Both are given to us by God and both raise us to the dignity of being collaborators with God; we are *causes* in our own right, not mere puppets. We receive our vocation from God, along with the supernatural tools, charisms, to fulfill it. On the other hand, our talents and hard-won skills allow us to make the carrying out of that work uniquely our own.

Although our talents, skills, and charisms work together in real life, for the purposes of discerning a charism, we must distinguish between them. Most of us know our talents and skills. What we don't know is how the Holy Spirit is empowering us to accomplish things that transcend our human abilities. Temporarily cutting our talents and learned skills away from the bundle of abilities we possess makes charisms visible. Unfortunately, in discerning charisms from talents, our inward experience and outward success may not be that helpful. As with a charism, we may experience joy, energy and satisfaction while using a natural talent. We may also achieve very successful results.

Charisms differ from talents in several key ways, and outward focus is one of the most telling. While we may be quite happy and successful using a talent mainly for our own personal enjoyment and growth, that won't be true of a charism. Charisms cry out for their intended recipients. They thrive and grow when we use them to serve others, and fade when we do not.

Supernaturally empowered, charisms can *only* be used for God's loving purposes. A talent, on the other hand, can be used to serve evil purposes. In fact, it takes genuine talent to be really effectively evil. Adolf Hitler was a very *talented* man. But a charism of the Holy Spirit can *never* be used for an evil end. You can't use a *charism* of writing to write hate literature or a *charism* of administration to run a drug cartel.

Charisms are also profoundly connected to our relationship with God. We often experience them as a kind of prayer or contemplation; they grow in power and purity as our relationship with God grows. By contrast, talents are more pedestrian and develop mainly with practice and technique. A charism cannot be separated from one's lived relationship with God—it is directly and immediately dependent upon grace, while a natural gift depends upon God at a much greater remove and is retained regardless of our relationship with him.

Finally, by giving us charisms, God empowers us to

Untangling charisms and natural talents

Charisms...

- Cannot be inherited from our parents.

- Are supernaturally empowered.

- Are profoundly and directly connected with our relationship with God, often experienced as a form of prayer, and grow in power and purity as our relationship with God grows

- Are directly and immediately dependent upon grace – while natural talents are retained regardless of one's relationship with God.

- Can only be used for God's purposes and to serve others, not to meet our own needs or for evil.

- Natural talents can be used not only for ourselves but for evil or for purposes that do not have God's redeeming work at the center.

9

successfully live our vocation; talent alone is not enough. For example, God sometimes gives people charisms where there is a notable lack of natural talent, even in areas where the person is otherwise extremely uncomfortable. A quiet, introverted person with a gift of Teaching may have an amazing impact as a speaker, experiencing great pleasure while communicating with an audience in spite of having difficulty in social situations at other times. In other cases, God gives people charisms that amplify and influence the direction of their natural talents, such as the naturally gifted physician whose charism of Mercy leads him to develop new methods to manage patients' pain. A call from God always comes hand-in-hand with the charisms needed to fulfill it. Charisms can therefore give us critical clues as to God's purpose for our life. If we're aware only of our natural abilities, we may not be able to discern and live that vocation.

Charisms versus other encounters with grace

The outward focus of the charisms also allows us to distinguish them from other encounters with grace we may have experienced. First of all, they are not the same as "consolations"–those delicious emotional rewards found occasionally in prayer, liturgical worship, devotions, meditation, and singing songs of praise. Nor are they to be confused with what are known as the Seven Gifts of the Holy Spirit, which we also receive at Baptism and Confirmation, but for our *own* benefit.[8] In the cases of both consolations and the Seven Sanctifying Gifts, grace is aimed at us, not at others *through* us. At the beginning of the discernment process, as people begin sifting through their spiritual experiences looking for the signs of a charism, there is often a tendency to confuse our experiences of the Seven Gifts and other encounters with grace with the inner feel of a charism in action. Just remember that not all religious experiences are charism-related; some are just between you and God. It's the outward focus that marks a charism. If there is no evidence that others are receiving the benefit of the gift, we have to question whether a charism is actually present, even if we personally experience great joy and pleasure in the activity.

On the other hand, thanks to their outward focus and supernatural results, others may recognize charisms in us that we have failed to see in ourselves. The same Spirit that gives us charisms for others often leads those others to ask us for them. This can be explicit, such as when someone says, "I always call you when I'm feeling down; you're *so* encouraging." Often, however, it's implicit. You might recognize a pattern in people's response to you, such as people repeatedly motivated to pursue a vision you've expressed, offering to help you achieve it (Leadership). In either case, you'll gain clarity if you deliberately test the potential charism by putting it in the service of others and watching their responses. If there is an authentic gift of Leadership fully at work, people will follow your initiative. If you have been given a gift of Teaching, people will learn. If it's Healing, people will get well.

Serving others is *the* central purpose of the gifts. *It's what they're for.* When we give our charisms that opportunity, they *will* make themselves felt. You can count on it. On the other hand, keeping charisms to ourselves by failing to exercise them in the service of others is one of the key ways we hinder, even prevent, them from appearing in our lives, no matter what else we may do to cultivate them.

> *"Freely you have received; freely give."*
> — *Jesus, Matthew 10:8*

---

[8] For more about the relationship between the charisms and the seven sanctifying gifts, see page 71.

10

Received: You can't achieve a spiritual gift

A charism is truly a gift. It can only be received, never achieved. This fact can be one of the hardest things to swallow about the spiritual gifts—*the fact that they are gifts*. It means two things: we can't "buy" them, and if we refuse to accept them they remain "unopened."

How might a person try to buy a charism? With prayer, with promises, with good works, with heavy investments of time and energy, with personal sacrifices, even with suffering. For us, it is almost automatic to think, "I want *x*, I think you want *y*; let's trade," or the more shadowy corollary, "I want *x*, maybe I can convince you to give it to me in exchange for *y*." These thoughts are basic ground rules for getting along in our economy, our relationships, our professional lives, and even in our families. Is it any wonder we so often invert the Golden Rule, not loving others *as* we love ourselves, but *so* we can get love *for* ourselves? Western culture not only esteems the ability to wield this "buying power," it lauds "self-made" men and women and the ability to "do it yourself," all of which can make it very hard to approach the discernment process ready to *receive!*

> *"Who can give a man this, his own name? God alone. For no one but God sees what the man is…Such a name cannot be given until the man* is *the name …to tell the name is to seal the success – to say "in thee also I am well pleased."*
>
> — *George MacDonald,*
> *George MacDonald: An Anthology*

God, of course, doesn't operate under this barter system, which is based on need. God has no needs. Because he is absolutely complete, whole, perfect, in and of himself, because he is in fact the creative Source of all things, he is utterly unsusceptible to our promotional offers! God gives simply because he wants to, out of pure delight and pure love. Discernment, therefore, is very much a process of finding out what it is he wants to give.

His beneficence doesn't mean, however, that our desires are irrelevant. As Jesus wryly made clear in the Parable of the Persistent Widow (Luke 18:1-8) and many other places,[9] it is good to ask God for what we want. We can ask for a charism, and God may give it. But God only gives us what is truly good, what will make us ultimately happy, and we don't always know what that is.

The danger lies in fixating on what *we* want. We can become so caught up in the asking and seeking that we become unable to receive. If you are like most of us, you are starting the discernment process with an eye on at least one charism you would really like to have. We can forget that our *desire* for a particular charism is no guarantee that God is going to give it to us. In fact, that desire can sometimes seriously hinder discernment of what God *has actually given* us—especially when we have a lot at stake. This wanting can distort our inner experience, leading us to mistake the excitement and longing we feel toward a particular charism with the energizing joy and peace of using a charism. Through our ambition to be a healer, a leader, or a writer, we become quite accomplished in the respective area due to our own hard work. We may, however, also refuse to admit ambiguous or negative results because so much is at stake for us.

You can see how desire for a gift could complicate and unnecessarily prolong discernment! Every day you spend maneuvering for a specific charism is one day longer

---

[9] *Matthew 7:7-11, Mark 11: 24, Luke 11:9-13, John 14:13*

11

you must wait to find out what God has prepared for you. The spiritual gifts are freely given, but to accept them we must stop creating ourselves in our own image and bow to the wisdom of our Creator. Receiving a charism is receiving part of our "new name," part of the face we now see only darkly. [10]

Lasting: Charisms you can discern are not temporary

Unless you're brand-new to the faith, your charisms have probably been with you a long time.[11] At Baptism and Confirmation, the Holy Spirit plants in each of us a special mix of gifts that will enable us to operate effectively as unique members of the Body of Christ, participating in the continuing work of salvation.[12] The charisms we can discern are distinct from temporary gifts—those one-time shots of grace the Holy Spirit sometimes provides out of the blue to empower people to respond to a particular situation. Charisms we can discern, on the other hand, are ways God *regularly* uses us in the world, over time, as his eyes, ears, mouth, or hands .

However, the charisms usually flower in our lives only after we turn our hearts toward the new life bestowed by the sacraments, that is, after we undergo a personal spiritual awakening and begin earnestly seeking to live our faith. This experience is often called by different names, such as "conversion," "renewal" or "Baptism in the Holy Spirit." Whether the experience is sudden and dramatic, or cumulative and quiet, the result is the same: you begin to seek God, to live as a disciple of Christ, and to open yourself to being used by the Holy Spirit. This is the soil that allows the seeds of the charisms to come into full bloom. The longer you've lived with a deep commitment to love and serve God, therefore, the more likely you are to have already experienced your charisms. And the more you deepen this commitment, the more your charisms will be able to grow. On the inside, the discernment process is an opening of your heart to God and to your neighbor.

The enduring presence of charisms has exterior implications for discernment, too. Because charisms are consistently present over time, they can be observed, tested and actively developed. When we "develop" a gift, we remove impediments to its use and situate ourselves so others can receive it. With greater opportunities available, the charism becomes more powerful: the Holy Spirit can operate through us more frequently and more directly. As a result, we will feel more definitively energized and achieve more dramatic or surprising results. Others will see this and recognize the presence of the charism—you may become "known for" the gift. In fact, developing gifts is the final key to discerning both charisms and call. As our charisms come to fruition, our efforts to discern them and to identify the life path they point to are satisfied. The goal of this workbook is to help you start that development. Before we get into that, however, let's look at your potential charisms.

---

[10] *Catechism of the Catholic Church* 1025, 2159; See *Revelation 2:17, I Corinthians 13:12* and *1 John 3:2*

[11] See the article on Baptism and Confirmation in *Additional Helps* (appendix) for further information about the connection between these sacraments and the charisms.

[12] See the *Catechism of the Catholic Church* 1266, 1304.

12

Deepening your commitment to God

If you haven't had the kind of spiritual awakening we've described, or would like to draw closer to the Lord, you might want to take a moment to deepen your commitment. The faith professed by the Church is personal and intimate. If your religious experience has been one of performing duties and rituals that are not an expression of your own inner love of the Father, Son, and Holy Spirit—you're missing the whole point! Jesus himself is the fullest revelation of God's will. When he says "Come, follow me," (Matt. 4:19) "I am the way, the truth, the life" (John 14:6) and we say "yes," we step onto a path, a whole new way of living, in which

- We are enabled to relate to God as a loving parent
- We are forgiven and are made able to forgive
- We are transformed in our ability to love and hope
- We gain a life and purpose that is eternal. That cannot be taken away. That is not dependent on the state of the economy, the esteem of others, or even our own achievements
  (See page 65 for additional information)

This life is open to every human person. It's yours if you ask for it and commit your life to God. If you want to, you can do it now.

Sit quietly a moment. Listen to Christ calling you: Come, follow me. If you are ready, tell him you do want to follow him. Tell him how much you want to be closer to him. Ask him to forgive all the wrong things you've done, or said, or thought. Ask for his guidance. Offer your life to him. You can do this in your own words, or use the following prayer.

> Holy One, I believe you sent your Son, Jesus, to show me the way to you. I believe in you and want to know you as you have revealed yourself in him. I deeply desire to be one of your children, to follow your Son, and draw closer to you. Forgive me for the evil things I have done. Guide me. Let me enter your love. I entrust my life to you. Show me the way. Amen.

Be silent. Listen. Notice what is happening inside you. Thank and praise God.

Making a personal commitment to God is only the beginning of the relationship. It's the proposal, not the marriage. If you are a Baptized Catholic, you can make good on your words by receiving the sacrament of Reconciliation and going back to Mass. You cannot follow Jesus fully and refuse to be part of the Church, because he established it as his Body on earth (Col. 1:18). If you are not Catholic and would like to find out more about participating fully in your Christian heritage, see page 73 and 74 of this workbook.

13

On Your Own: Explore Your Inventory Results, Prepare for Your Interview

During the initial *Called & Gifted Workshop*, you completed the *Catholic Spiritual Gifts Inventory* (if you haven't, do so before going on). We're going to spend a little time now reflecting on that experience, focusing on your six highest scores. If you're participating in the *Extended Discernment Program*, this exercise will help you prepare for your encounter with an Institute-trained interviewer. If you are using this workbook on your own, or with a self-organized discernment group, you will still find it helpful; although it cannot replace consultation with an experienced discerner.[13] For this reflection, you will need the *Inventory* book, your scores, and some paper (or your discernment journal if you're keeping one).

Please, don't mistake your *Inventory* results with discernment itself. Although taking it may well trigger recognition of a charism you've already been using, we are peering into mystery: the revelation of who God has created you to be. It's unwise to be too hasty or jump to conclusions. Tradition is clear on the need to *test* whether such things truly come from God.[14] It's best to think of the Inventory as working like a metal detector at the beach. It will turn up a lot of small change (which may well add up to part of the treasure you're looking for), some bottle caps, and, perhaps, a diamond ring. The difference is that seeking charisms isn't a matter of chance; we *know* the treasure is there. You do have charisms which God is infinitely more eager for you to receive and use them than you are yourself.

> *"Test everything; retain what is good."*
> — *St. Paul, I Thes. 5:21*

Take time to Pray

You are about to meditate on the ways God has worked in your life; it's good to begin with prayer. Please feel free to use the prayer provided, or make up your own. Here are some pointers:

❑ Take a moment to acknowledge and lay before God any concerns, conflicts, or other matters that may be weighing on your mind

❑ Think of who it is you are speaking with: the author of life, of all that is, the one who is only Good, the one who brought you into being

❑ Ask for guidance in your discernment, voice your longings; but pray also for the faith and wisdom to receive what you will be given

---

A Discerner's Prayer

Holy One, you are the Good Shepherd
who fills the hungry with good things,
who spreads a table before us,
who fills our cups to overflowing,
who calls each of us by name and leads us out.
Thank you for <u>all</u> of your gifts.

Today I am seeking to discern
those special gifts you have bestowed
to make me a channel of your love for others;
And to take these charisms up.

Open my eyes to your ways. Tune my ears to your voice.
Teach me what is important for me to know right now
as I reflect on who I am and the meaning of my life.
Especially, Lord, make the next step clear to me
and fire me with the desire to take it.

In the name of the Father, the Son,
and the Holy Spirit, Amen.

---

[13] You may be able to arrange a telephone interview by contacting the Institute.
[14] *Catechism of the Catholic Church*, 801

14

Reflect on your results

1) Sit quietly for a few moments, placing yourself before God. When you feel ready and recollected, take a look at your six highest-scoring charisms. Write these down, three on each side of a sheet of paper, leaving yourself a third of the sheet to make notes for each charism.

2) Do these high scores seem to match your experience? Why? Why not? For each gift you listed, briefly note your answer. Don't rush this. Allow yourself time to reflect fully on each.

3) For those gifts that seem to fit, can you describe when their effects first became apparent in your life?

4) After you have examined each of these six gifts, look up the one-page description of it in the *Catholic Spiritual Gifts Inventory* and read through it once more. Add any additional insights you may receive about your experience to your notes. Pay special attention to any parts or details of the charism that *do not* seem to describe you. You may wish to consult the *Key to Charisms*, found in the back of this workbook, which summarizes characteristics for each.

When you are finished, give each a preliminary 'rating':

❑ Make a **circle** the charism if it seems *probable* that it is one of your gifts—if your inner experience, objective results, and the response of others show **real evidence** of the presence of the charism.

❑ Put a **plus** sign next to those that seem *possible*—if there is **some indication** through at least one of the three signs (inner experience, actual results, others' response) that a charism is present.

❑ Put a **question mark** next to those about which you are *unsure*—the gifts in your top scores for which you can't see any of the signs very clearly.

❑ Put a **line through** charisms that you feel are *unlikely*—those you are **fairly certain** are **not** among your gifts.

On a second piece of paper, continue your reflection (Although perhaps not yet apparent, all of these questions are relevant to the discernment process,):

5) Do you, perhaps, have charisms that didn't score among the top six? Which ones? Why? Follow the same procedure as above and answer question three.

6) How comfortable are you with these charisms as a **set**? Do you have a sense of how your charisms might work together? How they might "help" each other?

7) Which of these gifts do you want to focus on discerning over the course of this workbook? You should choose one, especially one that you circled as being probable. (However, *we ask that you do not choose the charism of Faith* until you have already been through this process with another charism first. At this stage, it is too easy to confuse with the normal Christian virtue of faith.)

8) What questions do you have at this point about the nature, use, or working of any of these charisms? Note these to ask your Interviewer.

9) Do you have a sense that God has called you to a particular work of love (a vocation) in life? Can you put this call into words?

10) Do you have a sense of how your charisms are being used or could be used in different areas of your life? Your work? Your vocation? Your family? Other significant places?

The main goal of the interview is to help you identify patterns of giftedness already apparent in your life. This will enable you to choose a charism to discern that you do, indeed, likely possess and help ensure that you have a successful discernment experience. The interviewer cannot tell you whether you do or do not have a charism; he or she can only help you see the evidence of how God works through you. The discernment itself must find its basis in your lived experience.

After your interview, read all of Session 1 to prepare for your first group meeting.

Session 1: Ready, set, experiment

Discernment in Five Steps

Because of their four distinct characteristics—their supernatural source, their outward focus, the fact that they are received, and their enduring nature—charisms can be identified by their unique effect on us, on the world, and on the hearts of others. You can put this knowledge to work by choosing a charism you want to discern and deliberately trying to develop it, looking for the three signs we spoke of earlier: inner experience, effectiveness, and recognition by others (pg. 7). Here's how it works:

How to discern a charism

1) Choose the charism you want to test and try to approach it objectively

2) Experiment thoroughly with the gift by using it

3) Examine your **inner experience**

4) Evaluate your **actual effectiveness**

5) Weigh **the response of others**

Step 1: Put on your lab coat

Forget for a moment the longing you have to discern what God has in store for you. Set it aside. Instead, let's try to approach this process like a scientist might—with deliberate objectivity. Put on your "lab coat," if you will, and imagine you're a research technician out to design an experiment that will prove a theory: that charisms are real and you do in fact have some.

First, you need to spell out the specific "hypothesis" you want to test: for example, "I have a charism of Administration." You will explore the gift under the assumption you *do* indeed have it.[15] Once you've established what it is you will test, you need to gather some data about the charism so you know its "test requirements." These are the specific aspects you need to test to prove that this particular gift, not another, is present. You do this by going back to the description of the charism in your *Spiritual Gifts Inventory* and examining it again. Set aside your own experience and simply get to know the charism *itself.* You may want to consult the *Resource Guide,* a publication of the Siena Institute, which offers scripture references, citations from the Catholic tradition and further readings for each of the charisms. You will particularly want to examine the charism's key details, which are listed in the *Key to the Charisms* in the back of this book.

Focusing on the specifics of a gift is very important, because often it is a nuance of a charism, a distinctive detail, that makes discernment possible—both in distinguishing it from another charism, as well as from natural talents, experience, or developed skills. Your personal reaction to these details as you experiment will be telling.[16] For example,

---

[15] This approach works equally well with a gift you want to eliminate, one you want to discern you do *not* have. One or more of the three signs will be significantly absent. However, we encourage you to start with the gift you're most likely to have. The positive experience of having God work through you will give you an excellent yardstick against which you can measure other experiences effectively. Once you've acquired this, however, you may want to try the same process to rule out a gift. Eliminating a charism can be a great relief because it allows you to let go of an area of responsibility you're not equipped for, so you can focus on others that you are.

[16] If, when you examine the specifics of a charism, you have a strong sense that too many details do not fit you, you may want to choose a different charism to explore this time around. Ask yourself what other charism you might be seeing instead. You can look up the charism you wanted to explore in the *Key* in the back of this book to see possible alternative gifts it is often confused with.

looking in the Inventory, you see that the charism of Administration empowers a Christian to be an effective channel of God's wisdom by providing the planning and coordination needed to accomplish good things. Among the distinctive details of this gift, you find those gifted with Administration are *implementers* concerned with *solving the problems* of a *group or organization*, whose efforts are marked by *efficiency* and the ability to *delegate and coordinate* the work of a number of people. You know you love to organize, solve problems, and make things happen. But that part about delegating and coordinating…? You've done it so much at work, it could be a learned ability, not a charism. Your experiment, then, needs to test this aspect of the gift, which brings us to step two.

Step 2: Try the charism — experiment

After you have clarified what it is you are testing, you need to design and conduct your "experiment." You must explore the charism and its nuances in action. This is a matter of deliberately engaging in an activity that calls for the gift and "puts it through its paces." As you're planning your experiment, there are several issues to consider.

First, remember: the charisms are focused outward, so a proper test requires *serving another or others through the gift*. Reorganizing kitchen cupboards probably won't be an informative test of Administration—unless you do it for a harried friend who's been resolving for months to kick the McDonalds habit and get his cholesterol down.

Also, *a full trial should test the distinctive details of the gift*. Reorganizing your friend's cupboards doesn't tell you anything about your ability to delegate or coordinate the efforts of a number of people. You could as easily deduce you have charisms of Service or Wisdom, as Administration. Think of how a scientist might test your "hypothesis". You want to design an experiment that covers all of the distinguishing elements of the gift.

> ### Designing a thorough experiment
>
> - Choose an activity that engages the gift in the service of others
>
> - Make sure you do something that involves the charism's distinguishing details
>
> - Consider addressing a need you find compelling
>
> - Plan a reasonable timeline

But thinking of testing considerations are not the only things to consider. As you're choosing your experiment, don't neglect to consult your gut! If there is some act of service that you feel drawn to, something you feel really needs to be taken care of—listen. Often, but not always, such a feeling is a prime indicator of the Spirit tugging at your heart through a charism. This is especially true if the tug is a gentle one that often reminds you how *good* something is, and how *well* you could bring it about.

One more consideration: time. How long is it likely to take before you can expect to see results? At this point in your discernment adventures, it's wise to choose a discernment activity you can complete in less than two months. This workbook is designed for a six-week period, assuming the discerner spends at least **two hours per week** actually using the gift they're testing. Choose something modest. In fact, it's an excellent idea to take an activity that is already a part of your life and carry it out in such a way as to employ the charism you're exploring. Deliberately lean on the spiritual gift while you do your job, take care of your kids, support your spouse, spend time with friends, or do volunteer work you have already committed to.

Please note that using a charism does not have to be done within your church or even with fellow believers, although this is frequently where people start and can be a good place to experiment and get feedback. While it's true that the charisms are "for the renewal and building up of the Church,"[17] it's also clear throughout the Church's teaching on the subject from earliest times that this renewal and building is always meant in the context of her apostolic mission: to "go into the whole world and proclaim the gospel to every creature."[18] Some charisms, such as Pastoring, primarily build up the Church by serving the community of believers. But most are meant to bear Christ's love into the world. Often, that's where they have the most profound impact.

In a few pages, you'll find a worksheet to help you plan your experiment. The more carefully you "design" your experiment to (a) fully test the distinctive characteristics of the gift in the service of others, (b) satisfy a pressing need you perceive, and (c) yield results in a reasonable amount of time, the more information you will have when it's time to evaluate what happened. The three final steps of discernment can be monitored throughout the time you are experimenting with a charism: they involve looking for those three basic signs of a charism—your inner experience, actual effectiveness, and the response of others.

Step 3: Examine your inner experience – the first sign

Unless you have a fairly intense and well-developed faith life, your inner experience will probably be the earliest and most easily observed of the three signs—often apparent the moment you put a gift in action. We've mentioned this already: how *good* it feels when you're in the midst of using a charism. It's energizing and life-giving. You feel complete in what you're doing, as if you've found just where you "fit". You know what to do, without perhaps even realizing it, you just flow with the situation (even losing track of time) until suddenly you realize something good has happened and—delightfully—*you* were the vehicle.

If this sounds rather untidy and unpredictable, it is. We talk about "using" charisms, but in reality it works the other way around: charisms are ways the Spirit uses *us*. The Holy Spirit, of course, is notorious for flouting our attempts to put him on a schedule. Consequently, experimenting with a charism isn't simply a matter of acting, of deliberately exercising a certain ability. You cannot, for example, expect success if you announce to your boss it's time for *you* to lead, or if you decide to call a friend on the phone to dispense Wisdom. This is *not* likely to achieve heavenly results! Instead, you put a charism in action by seeking a situation that may call for the gift, showing up with the ears of your heart open, and then responding in the way that seems best.[19] You are presenting yourself, not *applying* yourself. "Activating" a charism, therefore, may be a bit like walking into a room and having someone hand you a box to carry outside: you respond. Or it may be more like walking into a room, seeing a box on the floor that needs to be carried outside, and taking care of it. Either way there is a real sense of receptiveness involved, of *receiving*—as with a gift. Which is why the felt experience of a

---

[17] *CCC*, 798; *Lumen Gentium* 12

[18] *Mark* 16:15

[19] For more on the ambiguity of discerning God's will, see *Acts 15* where the apostles discern on the issue of circumcision and announce "It seems good to the Holy Spirit and to us..." Also see *Isaiah 42:16 & 19* on the blindness of the Lord's servant.

charism often catches you by surprise: you find you have slipped into using a gift by no power of your own but openness.

Another important note about the subjective, inner experience of a gift-in-action: it can be surprising in it's distinctness from what you *expect* to feel. Like a child who procrastinates doggedly about taking a bath, only to splash around totally absorbed and complain with blue lips when it's time to get out, we can be highly reluctant to start an activity in which we have a spiritual gift—until we're actually doing it. This wincing resistance can continue in the early stages of using a charism, even when we're fairly sure we'll be fine once we get started! Sherry Weddell, co-founder of the Catherine of Siena Institute, whose presence as a speaker and teacher you may have experienced in a *Called & Gifted Workshop*, fainted out of pure terror after her first speaking adventure. Even today, in new and important situations, she usually feels some anxiety.

There can be several human causes for feelings of reluctance, especially fear of failure when we've got a lot of hope pinned on success. On the other hand, *long-term* reluctance or distaste is another matter; it probably indicates the lack of a charism. But be careful! Distinguish such distaste, which occurs over time, from what is merely an early "bad" experience. Such experiences are common and don't necessarily rule out the presence of a charism. They may, instead, indicate a supernatural gift in an area where you lack innate ability, comfort or skill. As you examine your inner experience therefore, it's crucial to focus on how you feel when you're actually using the charism, not how you feel before you start, or during related activities afterward.

The good news is the more you take up your charisms and the closer you draw to God, the less of this anxiety you experience. A joyous sense of flow, a living awareness of the goodness of the present moment and your presence in it—a fundamental quality of being in the Presence of the Most High—characterize the way it feels to use a charism. Charisms give you a taste of beatitude.[20] In addition, the more mature you grow in the Spirit and the closer you draw to Christ, the more this state of peace and well-being mark all areas of your life. Note, however, that *inner experience therefore becomes less and less useful* for discerning charisms as you grow in faith and spiritual maturity. For those who have walked closely with Christ for years, almost every experience of serving others can feel like a charism. That's when objective results and the responses of others become the truly essential test of supernatural empowerment.

Step 4: Evaluate your actual effectiveness – the second sign

It may take some time using a charism before your efforts have a visibly successful impact on a particular situation; there are many other forces at work than those operating through the charism. In fact, you may only be able to evaluate this at the end, though it's necessary to keep an eye on it as you go. Two things are good to remember. First, it's excellent to play the scientist, thinking always about concrete evidence that will prove the "hypothesis," what more you might do to test it, and when those results should show up. Second, you're not dealing with the laws of nature, but the one who authored it—so remain open to unexpected results!

The key question is: when you used the charism—especially the times you *felt* you might be using one—*did it actually do what it was supposed to*? When you taught, did you

---

[20] Beatitude is total happiness, the complete satisfaction of all our longings. It is not "Nirvana," the dissolving of self, but perfect fulfillment of *each individual* in communion with God. In Christian understanding, human beings were created for beatitude and will enjoy it forever in heaven.

see evidence that people learned? When you organized, did efficiency visibly improve? When you interceded for someone, was your prayer answered?

Another important question to ask: "Did the charism really achieve *supernatural* results in the situation? Why would you describe these results as unusual or surprisingly successful? Did this success bring about true goodness for all concerned? How did these results exceed what you would expect from your normal abilities, skills, and talents? Where did you get mediocre or poor results?

Talking in general terms about evaluating actual effectiveness makes it seem rather straightforward. But depending on what charism you're talking about, it may not be. Charisms like Teaching, Leadership, Administration, and Service often generate fairly easy-to-spot positive results. But the charisms of understanding—Wisdom, Knowledge, and Discernment of Spirits—are first about "seeing" or realizing something, and only second about acting on it. Their effectiveness, therefore, will be measured less well, perhaps, by visible results than by whether what you "saw" or realized was, in fact, true.

The creative charisms of Craftsmanship, Music, and Writing empower us to manifest truth and beauty in a concrete way. "Actual effectiveness" isn't so much whether people were moved by the creative work (which is really the third sign), but whether you "did justice" to the inspiration you received. Did the meal you made, the song you performed, the poem or the article you wrote, or the playground toy you built truly turn out the way you envisioned—or better? Only the maker can tell if an artistic charism was successful; it involves a qualitative sense of accomplishment.

Similarly, the effectiveness of the lifestyle charisms—Faith, Missionary, Celibacy, and Voluntary Poverty—must be judged by how much interior freedom they provide, and whether that freedom is actually lived out. Did Faith make it easy to take unusual risks with genuine confidence in God's protection and provision? Did the charism of Missionary make it a delight to enter an alien cultural situation and move with real effectiveness among the people? Has Celibacy kept you unencumbered and happily free of romantic relationships while empowering you to enjoy deep friendships? Does Voluntary Poverty enable you to live simply, truly freeing you from longings for created goods and struggles to acquire them? These charisms in particular underscore how important it is to clearly distinguish actual *effectiveness* from *people's response* to your endeavors.

If you find the actual results of your experiments less than supernaturally successful, put on your lab coat again: it doesn't mean your experiment has failed. It either means you need to experiment further, perhaps more thoroughly, or that you have successfully *disproved* your hypothesis. In discernment, success is recognizing where you are gifted *and* where you are *not*. To discern, you must be open to negative results and experiences, even though this can be painful. Exposing yourself to such possibilities is the only way to learn your true name. We will talk more about this in the next session.

Step 5: Weigh the response of others – the third sign

Finally, you must weigh the response of others. Depending on your personality and relational style, this can be the most frustrating part of discerning spiritual gifts. Confirming feedback can come in many forms. When it's direct—when someone tells you they've been touched in a profound way through your charism-led actions—it can be one of the high points of discernment. But too often, people *don't* offer such frank feedback. And it certainly can be awkward to ask! Imagine asking a friend if they ever feel inspired to trust God more when you share your extraordinary Faith. For some charisms, there's just no way to phrase the question without feeling you're being incredibly arrogant. This is one reason discerning with a group is so beneficial—they understand, share your intent and can tell you what they receive from you.

In reality, though, much of the feedback you receive will be *indirect.* For instance, you may find yourself always bumping into people who want to talk about their problems—a clue that the charisms of Encouragement or Wisdom may be present. Or "coincidence" may regularly place you with people who have questions about Christianity (Evangelism), or who are strangers to the area and need help entering the community (Hospitality). People will either run into you or seek you out for the gifts you have to give, often without knowing exactly why they are doing so. To the extent that you discern a pattern of such seeking, which seems to involve a specific charism, you can consider it confirming feedback.

In fact, if you use a gift in your community over time, you can expect such a "seeking pattern" to gradually change into one of appointment: you will find yourself asked to take on responsibilities or projects that fit your gift especially well. For instance, the clarity of vision you've expressed in the organization you work for may get you put in charge of a major project (Leadership). Or the knack for sewing you've demonstrated may first lead your church's liturgy commission to ask you to create Advent banners; then a fellow parishioner may ask you to help design a special quilt for the residents of the local retirement home where she works. When your community starts recognizing your gifts in this way, even if they know nothing about charisms per se, you may take it as fairly direct confirmation.

By the nature of some charisms, however, those who need to receive them do not initially seek them out. Until you recognize the gift, any seeking will seem coincidental. For example, Prophecy, in which a person is given sudden, inexplicable knowledge about someone else, often has its impact on the recipient because it comes as a surprise. Hospitality, with its orientation to welcoming outsiders and making strangers feel at home, tends to reach out to those whom reluctance keeps on the fringe. Mercy, too, may not be sought by those who need most to receive it, those beaten down by depression, misfortune, poverty, illness, or chronic suffering of some kind; they may not be physically able to seek it or to dare enough hope to ask for it. Mercy also gains much of its impact on the receiver when it's unexpected. Discernment of Spirits may elude our attention often because we don't seriously consider the objective existence of spirits. Other charisms that go largely unsought in their early stages are the creative charisms. Music, Writing, and Craftsmanship tend to urge their bearers to offer their gifts first— and the seeking-out comes afterward as confirmation.

The signs can come in any order

It's important to point out here that the three signs can come in *any* order, depending on circumstances. With Healing, for example, awareness of the charism often starts with a sudden experience of actual success, and "testing" is then a matter of confirming the ongoing presence of the gift and learning how it tends to operate in your life. Also, especially if you suffer a lot of anxiety or self-doubt, others may experience your charism before *you* feel it operating. It's possible to be so at war with yourself that you discount the real joy, pleasure, and quiet energy of charism-related activities. Taking seriously what others see in you can be a real eye- (and heart!) opener.

Finally, in certain cases, the two signs of actual effectiveness and others' response grow too entwined to separate. For charisms like Encouragement, Mercy, Hospitality, Teaching, Wisdom, Evangelism, Helps, Leadership, Missionary, Pastoring, and Prophecy, the impact of the charism is on the heart or mind of its beneficiary. Consequently, both the actual effect and the response of others manifest themselves at the same time. You know someone has been encouraged when you watch their energy rise or comforted when their suffering diminishes and their peace returns. These people may do something that shows they feel better. You know someone has felt welcomed when they warm up, relax, and feel free to be themselves. And later, they get involved in the community. You know someone is learning when you see "lights coming on" and later, application of that knowledge. You know wise counsel has struck someone when they express surprised and satisfied appreciation at your suggestion, and make a decision that turns out to be the right one. In these cases, the actual effectiveness of the charism can be demonstrated only by looking at others' responses—these charisms achieve their objective *within* the receiver.

If all this is making your head hurt, don't worry. It will become clearer as you focus on one specific charism. So let's do that. Let's see if we can build a discernment plan for the charism you've chosen to explore.

On Your Own: Design your discernment plan

The basic goal of this session is to actually get you started discerning a charism in action, the next step beyond analyzing your past experience, or reading and thinking about what the gift looks like. This reflection will lead you through the first two of the five steps of discernment we just described. If you're discerning in a small group, you'll have the chance to discuss and improve the experiment you come up with today when you hold your first small group meeting.

For this reflection exercise you will need:
- About one hour of quiet time
- *The Catholic Spiritual Gifts Inventory* you received at the Called & Gifted Workshop
- Your *Discerner's Workbook*

Optional but very useful would be:
- *The Catholic Spiritual Gifts Resource Guide* (also available from the Institute)
- A Bible
- A copy of *Catechism of the Catholic Church* (currently available on the Internet at *www.Christusrex.org/www1/CDHN/ccc.html*).

Find a comfortable place to sit and write. Quiet yourself and ask the Holy Spirit to be with you. Ask God to help you see whatever you need to in order to discern his loving purposes for your life. You might use the Discerner's Prayer on page 14. When you are ready, spell out what your "experiment" aims to prove using the following outline:

What "hypothesis" are you testing? Fill in the blank:

"I have a charism in _____."

Look up the charism you've chosen to explore in the *Spiritual Gifts Inventory*:

What is the specific definition of this charism?

What are its key distinguishing details? *(See the Key to the Charisms in back.)* **Which do you think may describe you? Which do you suspect may not?**

For those with a copy of the *Catholic Spiritual Gifts Resource Guide:*

To get an even better idea of the charism, open your *Resource Guide* to the gift in question. Read the scriptural references related to the gift. Look up the passages in the *Catechism.*

What do these passages have to say about the charism? What role has it played in the life of God's people? How does it reveal God's loving purposes? What does it tell you about him?

How do you feel about a possible call to be a bearer of this gift?

If you have reservations, fears, or doubts at this point, that's not a bad thing. Take a moment to note them. A certain amount of skepticism is excellent for discernment. Also, think about reading one or more of the recommended books or the life of one of the "patron saints" listed for the charism in the *Resource Guide* to further strengthen your understanding of how the gift may look in practice.

Now let's think about your experiment.

What could you do right now, this week, that calls for this gift? Where could you present yourself where this charism might be needed? List as many possibilities as you can think of; small-scale is fine.

Of these alternatives, which ones put this gift in the loving service of someone else? (Circle)

Which of them test distinguishing details of the gift? Note which details.

Are there any distinguishing details of the charism that are not being tested? How might you test them?

How could you explore those details of the charism you're not sure apply to you?

Of all these possible "experiments," which seems most pressing to you? Which do you feel is something *you* can do to meet an unmet need you've noticed? Are there any other situations around you which you have not listed, yet which you feel something related to this charism "needs to be done"?

How much time are you likely to need to commit to these activities before you can realistically expect to see results? Which will fit into the six weeks you have to experiment if you're in a small group?

25

Choose one (or part of one) of these experiments for each of the next six weeks.

Week 1:

Week 2:

Week 3:

Week 4:

Week 5:

Week 6:

You can begin experimenting right now. If you're discerning on your own, you should spend a couple weeks at it before going on to Session 2. If you're in a small group, read on.

Discerning Together: Your first small group meeting

If you're meeting in a small group to start discerning your spiritual gifts, you've made an excellent decision. Remember, though, that people come to small groups looking for different things. The participant of few words, for example, may feel alienated from the group if the discussion gets too far off topic or bogs down too long with one person. Some people need information; they come to gain knowledge from the group. Others come because they long to be seen and heard. They need to be affirmed and recognized by the group, and may unwittingly dominate the group's attention. An effective, valuable small group discernment experience requires that everyone respect the needs of both without allowing the focus of the group to derail. At some point, your needs or expectations will probably clash with those of someone else; you must be prepared to listen and make room for them, and to listen to and make room for yourself.

Discernment, in its fullness, cuts to the root of our dreams and hopes: it seeks to lay bare the truth about who we are and why we're here. Everyone is vulnerable at this level and deserves the greatest care. Thus, it's crucial that everyone in the group agrees to create and maintain an atmosphere of humility and respect for each other. Several ground rules will help ensure the group experience is valuable for everyone.

> *"Conduct yourselves in a manner worthy of the call you have received, with all humility and gentleness, with patience, bearing with one another through love."*
> — *St. Paul, Eph. 4:1-2*

26

Ground Rules

❑ **Everything shared is confidential**

The experiences people share during this process are not for casual consumption. Protect each other's privacy. You may learn things about each other that surprise you.

Also, in the process of describing your own experiences with a charism, remember that you may need to protect the privacy of those who received the fruit of your charism—they came to you, not to your whole discernment group. Have you been encouraging a neighbor contending with an abusive spouse? Using Knowledge to help someone free themselves from a debt-ridden financial situation? Be discreet. Focus on what happened; leave identities ambiguous. This can be an issue even with seemingly impersonal organizational charisms such as Leadership, Administration or Service because they may call you into action where someone else has dropped the ball. Protect the identities of the people involved even if someone failed through selfishness.[21] Charisms are for the building up of the Body of Christ, never for the tearing down of *any* of its members.

❑ **Stick with Discernment**

Remember that time is limited and you have gathered to help each other discern charisms. Come early, or stay after, if you want to catch up with a friend. Also think about the fact that some in the group may feel like strangers. Chatting too much during group time with one person you like may leave others feel isolated or excluded.

❑ **Voice your needs**

If you happen to be the one who feels excluded, or if the discussion has gone off track, speak up, at least to one other person in the group. Don't tune out! Your authentic participation is important not only to your own discernment but to the success of others as well.

If you feel you need more attention from the group in order to discern successfully, try to pinpoint where your need lies. You can ask for what you need directly during discussion, though any lengthy response should be given outside the discussion time. You will also have the opportunity to ask people to pray for your specific needs at the end of every meeting. One of the great benefits of discerning in a group is being able to receive the Encouragement, Wisdom, Knowledge, Mercy, Help, Faith, Pastoring, Service, Leadership and other charisms God has given others. Voicing your needs will often draw out the charisms of others in the group, and give you an opportunity to receive God's love and grace.

First Meeting Agenda

1) Open with a prayer *You may want to:*

- *Thank God for the opportunity to meet and the presence of these unique, gifted individuals*

- *Mention the ultimate objective of discernment—the growth of each person into his or her role in God's saving work in human history*

- *And request that God reveal the next step for each person*

2) Discuss ground rules

3) Introduce yourselves to each other

4) Answer the Discussion Questions

5) Ask for prayer intentions in this process; closing blessing

---

[21] See *Matt 18:15, James 3*

❏ **If you have an opinion—share carefully**

We all have the Christian role of mentor. Even if you don't have the gift of encouragement, you can help others discern and develop their gifts, and they can help you. Your prayers, your attention, your experiences, your insights, and your encouragement can be priceless aids to those pursuing this process with you. Also, you will be sharing with each other what you learn as you explore your chosen charism (which others may also have if you're in a gift group built around related charisms). As you listen to others' discernment experiences, you will probably notice things you want to point out to them. Here are a few points to keep in mind:

Firstly, the bearer of the charism is the primary discerner of God's call. You cannot discern a gift for someone else. The person always has the final responsibility for his or her own discernment. Therefore, honor this rule:

Never tell anyone that they *do* or *do not have* a particular charism.

Secondly, however, you can assist others' discernment. Don't give final answers but *do* share insights. Condition your language, report what you "see." This can be tremendously clarifying for people trying to make sense of their subjective experiences. You assist another to discern by:

❏ Listening carefully to his or her actual experience of being used by God
❏ Helping the person recognize patterns in his or her life
❏ Pointing out specific evidence in his or her life experience that may indicate the presence of a particular charism
❏ Describing in specific ways what you seem to receive from each person.

Third, remember that you are a companion, not a therapist, career counselor, vocation director, or diviner of the future. You do not have to answer the question, "What should I do?" for the person struggling next to you. In fact, to the extent you give people answers, you are undercutting the very point of discernment for them: learning to listen and respond to God's call. Share your insights, but let them develop their own answers. Encourage them to grow! If someone seems to need *professional* counsel, of course, you should make the suggestion as prudence directs.

Finally, create an atmosphere of respect in little ways. Make eye contact while listening to others. Allow a moment of silence after someone describes an experience; don't immediately offer your insight. After all, they've just shared an encounter with grace, or at least an account of seeking God! If there are those who seem reluctant to speak, respect their reserve but consider drawing them out with a thoughtful question that shows you're truly interested.

Introductions

After you've established the ground rules, go around the group and introduce yourselves briefly. Tell three things: your name, any vital facts about who you are, and then briefly describe the family, work, community, spiritual, artistic, or intellectual involvements that are important in your life. Each person should take just a couple minutes. On the next page, you'll find a sheet you can copy or use to take notes about each of your fellow discerners. You'll want this information later; between meetings, you'll be praying for each other.

28

Discerning Together—a worksheet to help you assist fellow discerners

Use this tool to remind yourself how to pray for others in your discernment group as you go through this process.

Name	Charism	Prayer requests	Your observations

Discussion Questions

Take the next hour and a half to answer the following questions. Take five to ten minutes to reflect silently on these questions and then share your answers. Go around the table and let everyone answer one question before moving on to the next. This method helps ensure that no one takes too long or gets off the subject. It also helps people strike a balance between focusing on their own discernment and having concern for the discernment efforts of all the others. You may find it helpful to take a few notes as others talk so that you can better pray for them throughout the program.

What charism are you exploring and why did you pick this gift? Have you explored or used this charism before? How?

How are you planning to experiment with or explore this charism during this program? Describe what you plan to do in detail. Do you have any questions or concerns about experimenting with the charism you have chosen?

Why did you decide to begin discerning your charisms? What are you seeking from God?

Prayer intentions and closing blessing

How would you like the other members of the group to pray for you until you gather for the next session in two weeks?

To close the session, go around the table and allow each person to answer this question. Note their answers—and anything else that may have occurred to you to put before God on their behalf—on the sheet on page 29. Finally, pray together thanking God for what has been shared in the group and asking his blessing and guidance for each of you as you go forward seeking his will. You may want to close the session by saying together:

Come, Holy Spirit!
Fill the hearts of your faithful
Enkindle in them the fire of your Love;
Send forth your Spirit
And they shall be created,
And you shall renew the face of the earth.

Between now and Session 2, put one or two of your experiments into action. You may wish to take notes on what happens when you do the activity that calls for the charism: what your inner experience is like, whether you see any actual results, how others react or respond. Once you get going, you may also want to look again at the material describing the charism, do some of the additional reading, and adjust or add to your experiment. In the next section, we will talk more about the experience of progressing through the discernment process.

Something to try: **Make your experiment a prayer**

As you begin exercising the charism you are exploring, we encourage you to make each experiment a prayer offering. Every time you seek to use a charism of the Holy Spirit, you are opening yourself to be a conduit of God's power and love—a pipeline between Heaven and Earth. You can keep that line clear with prayerfulness before, during, and after you use the charism:

Before: Don't jump into the situation too quickly. If possible, take at least a moment to place yourself, your gift, and the situation before God. Open yourself to his provision. Acknowledge that you do not know for certain what God intends here or what will happen. Ask that he will use you to bless this person (or people) in this situation, here, now.

During: Use your charism with attentiveness, watching what seems to be happening. Try to avoid forcing a certain outcome. Keep track of how the gift may be doing what it is supposed to. Remain aware that God is working out his mysterious plans, and that you are obediently helping with this little act of service.

After: Deliberately release what you have done, and the people you served, to God. Place the whole encounter in his hands. If you find yourself experiencing disappointment or other negative feelings because something did not turn out as you had hoped, look at where these might be coming from and then try to let them go. If you find yourself replaying conversations or events in your mind, do something that will bring your attention back to the present moment and whatever it asks of you. If you are working, you can focus on some challenge. If it's time to rest, read a book, immerse yourself in music, or really *savor* that cup of coffee. Let God have the encounter. When it's time to use your charism again, be ready for a whole new adventure.

31

32

Session 2: Deepening your discernment

At this point, you have hopefully spent time—at least four hours—actually trying to use the charism you are discerning. In this section, our goal is simple: to help you look carefully at what happened, then *deepen* your discernment in order to get beyond early conclusions, premature judgments, and the inner anxieties that often well up in this process. We're going to focus on observable facts in light of the three signs, and then describe some effective ways to deal with what you've observed.

After your experiments, you will find yourself in one of four situations:

1. **Apparent contradiction:** your experiments lead you to doubt the presence of the gift
2. **Apparent zero, goose egg, dud:** your experiments seem to yield no useful information either way
3. **Apparent confusion:** your experiments yield mixed signals
4. **Apparent confirmation:** your experiments point toward the presence of the charism

In any of these situations, it's important to keep experimenting and discerning. Yet it's all too easy to stop, to assume we do or do not have a charism, or that we'll never really be able to know for certain. In fact, we may do this without really realizing it.

From bushwhacking to orienteering: Finding your way along the discernment trail

It's difficult to hold the tension of not knowing. This process of trying to discover the special way Christ is calling us to bring his love to others comes with a growing longing for clarity. We want to see exactly what he wants, now that we know he wants something unique from us. We may well get glimpses and snatches of light as we go. You may have received a few of these already in your charism experiments; or you may not have. This process can take time.

Much of the journey is an overland hike through a jungle of competing attractions, pressures, questions, decisions, outcomes, and encounters with others. Our ongoing temptation is to take the machete of our own judgment and start hacking our way forward—acting from what *we* think instead of remaining tentative and being directed by what actually happens when we use a gift. This hacking results in a trail all right, but it's a trail of our own making, not one we have discerned. Discerning the trail of a charism in your life necessitates moving from willful bushwhacking to "orienteering"—consulting the map and compass of your actual experiences before cutting your path. Let's look at where in the jungle of this process you may find yourself and how to orient yourself to true north.

On Your Own: What happened when you used your gift?

First, we'll look at the map: the factual details of an incident in which you tried to exercise a charism. You must first chart the terrain of what you did, who was involved, and how events unfolded in order to find reference points that will help you discern. That will be part one of this reflection. In part two, we'll lay the compass of the three signs on top of that experience to see which direction you should take. You'll need about half an hour for this exercise. You may want to photocopy the questions below if you wish to explore more than one encounter with a charism.

Part I: Log your experience

Take a moment to commend yourself to God with a prayer for help in discerning his will. Then, reflecting on a single, significant (though not necessarily recent) time when you exercised or experimented with the charism you are now exploring, answer the following questions:

- What prompted you to act in this situation? Why did you do it? (a request from others, seeing a need, experiencing a "prompting" or call of the Holy Spirit, I was doing something else and it "just happened", etc.)

Describe in step-by-step detail exactly what took place. Include the following information:

- What, specifically, did you do to use the gift? Describe your actions.

- Who were you with? Were you alone, with one other person, a small group, a team, a large group, a small mob? And if you were with others, what was your relationship to them? Were you a helper, a friend, spouse or family member, a care-giver, a contributor, an acquaintance, a team member, a partner, or a leader?

- Where were you? Describe the situation or circumstances of your encounter.

Part II: Look for the signs

As you examine this experience, use the three signs of a charism—inner experience, actual effectiveness, and the response of others—to sift through what happened. Try to remain objective, just noting the facts. In a few pages, we'll address where you might find yourself in relation to what happened. So, remembering the incident you just described…

What was it like to use this gift? Describe your inner experience while using the gift in as much detail as you can. Be specific. Note anything that you sense as being part of your relationship with God.

What was the short-term result of what you did? Do you have a sense of the long-term result? Describe what you observed. Did the charism do what it was supposed to?

Did other people respond to what you did at the time? How? Have you received any feedback from others about how *they perceived* what you did?

Do you consider this experience to have been successful? If so, why? If not, why not? What do you think success would have looked like in this situation?

To deepen your discernment, look for a pattern

At this point, you may have developed some suspicions about the presence of this gift. They may be positive. Or, they may be negative, even downright painful. In either case, it's important not to stop here. If you let yourself slip into conclusions about your charisms at this point, you are no longer discerning. You're hacking your way alone. You need to discern until you illuminate a *pattern*.

Patterns are the key to true discernment. Real confidence in the possession of a charism only comes from recognizing repeated, consistent evidence that God uses you in a specific way to bring his purposes and love to people. The same is true when *eliminating* charisms. You need to identify a pattern of personal indifference or distaste for the activity; of mediocre or poor results; of merely polite, bland, or negative responses from others before you can rule out a charism. Obviously that

35

cannot happen in two weeks! It may not happen in six. In fact, it could take several years, depending on the breadth and depth of your experience. Therefore, a major part of the work of discerning charisms involves creating opportunities either for the pattern of evidence regarding your giftedness *to accumulate in your life*, or for the pattern *to emerge from your past and become visible*.

For those with limited experience in using a particular gift, discernment will involve experimenting in order to acquire enough experience for a pattern to form. If you already have a lot of experience in the area, discernment will involve experimenting to highlight and recognize *already existing* patterns of effectiveness and to clarify any unexplored facets of the charism. Which category describes your situation with this potential gift? Take a minute to answer the following three questions about experience because it will affect how you go on. You may need to deliberately *suspend judgment*, avoiding any definitive conclusions so you can keep experimenting. On the other hand, you may need to *come to judgment*, examining patterns of experience in order to discriminate non-charism related experience from areas of true giftedness.

How long have you been seriously living your faith?

This is an important question because as we've mentioned before, there is a real relationship between the depth of your relationship with God and the emergence and growth of your charisms. What do we mean by "seriously living your faith?" We're not talking about casual practice (attending church occasionally or only for major holidays, weddings, and funerals), or a merely cultural identity ("Of course I'm Catholic. I'm Irish or Polish or Italian or Filipino, aren't I?"), or even attending church for the sake of being part of a friendly or nourishing community. Seriously living your faith means

- ❑ a faith and a practice that is deeply *personal*,
- ❑ a sincere desire and intention to follow Jesus as a disciple,
- ❑ a life marked by prayer, effort to grow in one's faith and knowledge of God,
- ❑ active participation in your local Christian community even if it is a sacrifice.

Generally speaking, people start to see their first charisms emerge a year or two after the point where their faith becomes conscious and personal. Since your charisms are gifts of God to the community, the involvement in service to others, which is a natural part of growing as a disciple, becomes a great way to explore possible charisms.[22]

How long have you been actively involved in using the gift you're exploring?

The issue here is how much practice you've had doing the activity. Have you been a teacher for thirty years? Or did you just volunteer as a catechist two months ago? Have you been studying and practicing art for several years? Or did you take a painting class recently and discover you love it? For our purposes, someone "with a lot of experience" in the activity is *someone who has been using the gift seriously for a year or more* (though not necessarily an "expert" or "professional"). If you've been interested for a long time, even if you've read about it with great diligence, you must consider yourself still a beginner in this charism if you haven't tried doing it. Remember, we

---

[22] See the box on page 13 if you would like assistance praying for greater closeness to Christ at this time.

36

need enough raw experience to establish a pattern. If you don't have a large handful of encounters already to draw from, you need to focus on acquiring more, otherwise you'll be judging from limited evidence.

How much have you used this gift for *others*?

Finally, you should consider your experience using this aptitude for others. This is an important clue to how you should proceed. Reluctance to use a gift in "public" can be a sign you're not ready to look critically at it; you may need more affirming experiences to develop your confidence. Alternatively, it could signal, not a lack of confidence, but the private nature of the activity. Perhaps it is just for you. If you've written a lot of poetry, but haven't shared it much because it's "just for me", or if you unloose your rich tenor voice to sing in the car but have never joined the choir, you may need to respect your instinct to keep this activity private. Along with a charism usually comes a desire to share it with others. If this impulse to share is completely absent, it's unlikely that a charism is involved.

If it's just lack of opportunity or confidence that has kept you from sharing with others, this is a good time to begin. If you really want to explore this gift, you need to give yourself plenty of time and opportunities to share it publicly before you allow yourself to make judgments about its status as an actual charism.

If your answers to these three questions place you in the inexperienced category—if you've become serious about your faith only within the past year,[23] if you've only dabbled in the activity, or only done it privately—you'll want to avoid making judgments. Instead, focus on continuing your experiments to get relevant experience in whatever area you need more information.

If your answers made it clear that you *are* experienced in this area, your problem may be how to successfully sort all the experiences and input that you have into meaningful patterns. You may have acquired such a broad range of experiences and skills that you can't discern where you should focus your energies, and identifying areas where you are not gifted would be a positive relief! In this case, you need to focus just on what seems relevant to the charism you are discerning and cut out what does not.

Where do you fall? With your level of experience in mind, let's look at four different attitudes you may have developed at this point toward the charism you are exploring and see how to step from them into deeper discernment. If your experience has not yet led you to one or more of these scenarios, it's good to read through them anyway—for the sake of your discernment group, as well as for yourself. You will encounter most of them personally at some point as you continue to discern additional charisms in the future; they describe different phases of the discernment process.

On page 49, a pattern-finding worksheet will help you pull together the following material and apply it to your own situation. Take a peek at this now; you may want to photocopy it and keep it beside you as you read. Or, you may wait and tackle it after

---

[23] If this describes you, learn about the charisms but don't worry if no charisms seem to have emerged yet. It may be too soon for that. It really does take a couple of years to absorb and integrate what it means to live as a disciple and it is normal that charisms become visible as we do so. All that you're learning about discernment through this process will prepare you to recognize and welcome your charisms when they do emerge.

37

you are done, perhaps after letting the information percolate for a day or two. (Please note that we have designed both the initial reflection in this present session and the pattern-analysis worksheet as tools you can use again and again. They will help you to examine individual incidents in detail and chart charism patterns in your experience any time you want to discern a charism more closely.) *If you become confused or overwhelmed by the amount of information given in this section, please just focus on the situation that best applies to you. (Skip to page 42 for Apparent Confusion, or page 46 for Apparent Confirmation).*

I) Apparent contradiction: when the charism looks doubtful

Nothing can make people shy away from further discernment more speedily than an initial experience which seems to say, "Sorry, no charism here." If your efforts to explore a charism have left you doubting a gift you thought you might have, hold on! The show's not over yet.

There are two possible situations. You may be looking at an isolated instance or two from limited experience, such as when a person's first few attempts to personally assist someone have not helped move a complex project forward. He may seriously question the presence of the charism of Helps and begin to wonder if he really just wanted to be valued by someone he admired. On the other hand, you may be facing an event that seems to bring a pattern of past and disconfirming experiences into focus. For example, you've been exploring a charism of Hospitality and throw yet another informal dinner party. For what seems like the twentieth time, you find yourself paying such rapt attention to a single person that you burn the garlic bread and forget to refresh people's drinks. You realize you're cussing silently at the necessity of these mannerly details, wishing you could have just one hour at a café with each one of your guests. Suddenly you see that you've never really enjoyed putting these events together.

Neither of these example experiences actually tells you anything definitive about the presence of a charism, though you may feel as if they do. Both forms of apparent contradiction in fact call for further discernment. We'll address the issues of limited experience first.

How to suspend judgment in the face of apparent contradiction

If your experience in personally and seriously living the faith (cf. above, pg. 36) or with the activity involved in your experiment is only recent, there may be several explanations for apparently contradictory results. It may be that you simply haven't allowed enough time for the charism to develop. Or factors such as poor timing, interpersonal issues and circumstantial complications may have hindered your efforts. In the Helps example given above, for instance, a temporary crisis may have overshadowed his contribution, making it seem irrelevant for a time. Finally, if you misunderstood the nature of the charism, you may have developed faulty expectations, or tested it the wrong way. Here is what you can do to suspend your disbelief and keep discerning:

■ **Look again at what you actually did to use the gift**. Try to take note of all the details of the situation—the who, what, when, where, why and how—and consider what else might account for the fact that your experiment was negative. Did circumstances conspire against a positive outcome? For example, were you scheduled to facilitate a faith-sharing group that was cancelled due to snow? If you never got people together, you couldn't test

38

Copyright © 2000

a charism of Pastoring. Did you present to the wrong audience? If you tried your Pastoring experiment within a long-established group you've been part of in which people expect to spend most of their time socializing, you may not have given the charism a fair opportunity.

■ **Look at the characteristics of this charism and consider whether what you did to explore the gift was truly a valid test.** Were you testing *your* idea of what this gift is rather than the gift itself? The charism of Giving is not giving of yourself or of your time. Nor is it "giving until it hurts." Rather, it's an unusually generous distribution of your material wealth with *glee*. Likewise, the charism of Helps is not the virtue of being helpful and kind to the people in your life. It is an energized desire to use your special charisms and talents to help a particular individual achieve a *significant* mission—not just anything they're trying to accomplish.

Also, your test must involve *actually using* the gift. Let's say you were discerning a charism of Teaching and you'd long thought there was a real need in your church for deeper adult formation in the faith. You decide to test the charism by putting together a proposal describing how the parish could provide a study group on the *Catechism*. You give it to your pastor. His response is politely appreciative, but he does nothing with the idea. What's wrong with this picture? It's not a valid experiment for Teaching![24] It may say something about your pastor's current

---

The significance of coincidences and mystical 'signs' in discerning what God wants

It's quite common for people who begin watching for evidence of charisms to become sensitive to "meaningful coincidences" or "mystical signs" that seem to confirm or deny the presence of the charism they're exploring. These "signs" may range from discovering that the patron saint of the charism you chose has the very name you chose for Confirmation, to unexpectedly receiving roses or a blessed object.

Try to cultivate a healthy skepticism in this area.

While it is true that God does sometimes give such signs, both Scripture and the teaching of the Church are clear on the fact that signs are *not* the normal way we are to discern his will. Moreover, they must always to be tested in the light of objective evidence (*Catechism of the Catholic Church* 2111, 2115-16).

In fact, following the breadcrumb trail of coincidence is contrary to the spirit of discernment, which entails stepping forward into the darkness of possibility, acting in faith, and watching for what happens. The charisms are objectively real; they do what they are supposed to do and they leave observable evidence. We can choose to use a charism, but we do not control the outcome. There are all kinds of unintended effects and repercussions when we use a gift. When you look for mystical signs, on the other hand, you tend to impose your own meaning on the events. Not only do you miss much of what God is doing in the situation, but, instead of letting God lead, you usurp for yourself an illusion of control.

In particular, beware the temptation to try to make God do things your way. It can be almost unconscious, such as when you set up 'opportunities' for God to let you know his will. You hear yourself thinking ,"Here's your chance, Lord. If this happens, I'll know you're telling me I have this gift." But if the event is not directly relevant to the charism in question, you are actually asking God to circumvent the normal discernment process with a mystical signal. You should realize that the objective value of such omens is largely *useless* because you have no way to judge their authenticity. God has chosen to forgo directly controlling the actions of his creatures—neither the wind that topples a tree nor the philanthropist who builds hospitals. We simply cannot interpret events as windows on God's opinion, however tempting this may be!

---

[24] This example might actually serve as a good test for the insight-sharing and practical solution-finding gift of Wisdom.

priorities or level of trust, but it says nothing about your giftedness because *you didn't actually teach anything to anyone.* A valid experiment would be to gather a few friends and try teaching for a few weeks on a subject that you are particularly interested in.

■ **Make sure you're not using a gift to serve someone too close to you.** Families are usually not the best place to start your discernment. Your relationships with those closest to you may be so tied to what they need from you as a spouse, parent, sibling or child that their responses to your experiments may be too complex to decipher. Try exploring the gift with friends, neighbors, coworkers, or people you don't know so well, and who don't have so much invested in you. If you have a very small group of acquaintances, this will mean that you need to break out of the norm a little and expand your circle of relationships. God himself says that it's not good for us to be alone.[25] If your life circumstances have left you in an isolated situation, take steps to reconnect with your community.

■ **Finally, look again at the evidence of the three signs. Did you discount positive evidence?** Sometimes people are looking only for a certain kind of feedback as a sign of the charism, such as recognition from a certain person like a spouse or pastor, or some pre-determined outcome. Make sure your expectations realistically fit the description of the charism as written. Approaching a gift experiment with an underlying agenda, such as when you really wanted to prove something or to be recognized by others, is very likely to make you overlook or discount information that doesn't support your agenda—even strong, positive evidence of a charism.

All of us will have a time or two when we try to use a charism and apparently nothing happens. For those who have a lot of experience using the gift they're exploring, such episodes will carry much less weight. The more experience you have using the gift, the more you'll focus on the pattern and not get caught up in any one incident. You'll tend to see results as inconclusive, rather than contrary to, the gift.

What a true "no" looks like

The realization of contradiction, after many attempts, can happen suddenly: you try to use the gift in one more situation and **click!** the results illuminate a pattern running through many experiences that points decidedly away from the likelihood of a charism. Despite all the times you've stepped forward with a promising idea about how to make things better in your parish, your office, your faith-sharing group, your community club, you always seem to end up struggling to implement the plan single-handedly, and you realize no one seems to follow your leadership. The actual effect of the charism of Leadership just isn't there…and never really has been.

This is not necessarily a negative experience. Often it's a great relief. You have identified an area in which you no longer need to be so highly responsible, an area into which you've been pouring energy and time and have not perhaps reaped a comparable return—in personal enjoyment, actual success, or positive impact on others.

Sometimes, though, it isn't a relief, but a source of grief. The more experience you've had in this activity, the more you're likely to be personally invested in it. It may

---

[25] *Genesis 2:18*

be a significant part of your sense of identity. You may even consider it a key to your happiness. Facing evidence that this is not one of the ways God has empowered you with a charism can feel like giving up an essential part of yourself. When you reach this point, you may want to go through the considerations mentioned above just to make sure that there is no other explanation for the apparently negative results you've recognized; but then it's time to let go. It's time to make a leap of faith, to truly live your belief that God is Good—to remind yourself, as Blessed John Henry Newman did, that

> *God has determined, unless I interfere with His plan, I should reach that which will be my greatest happiness. He looks on me individually, He calls me by my name, He knows what I can do, what I can best be, what is my greatest happiness, and He means to give it to me. God knows what is my greatest happiness, but I do not.*[26]

This juncture can be one of the most difficult areas of discernment—when we have to absorb a major revision of who we think we are. It can be hard to remember that this is why we started the process in the first place! So, while you give yourself time to grieve what you've lost, also take a moment to let this sink in: *you have successfully discerned.* In fact, you may have just realized something about whom you were created to be that you would never have been able to see in any other way. However, you don't have to go away empty-handed.

■ **Is a different charism possibly involved?** You have been engaged in this activity for a long time. You've come back to it again and again. You've been successful at it and enjoyed something about it. Why? What kept drawing you? *Chances are very good there is another charism involved.* Check the *Key to Charisms* for possible alternatives to the charism you've just ruled out. If it's not Leadership, might it be Administration? If it's not Pastoring, could it be Teaching? How do the three signs stack up if you look at your experiences through the lens of the alternative charism? You can step deeper into discernment now by adjusting your experiments and reflections to test between the two possibilities.

II) Apparent zero: you tried it and nothing happened

Sometimes people conclude that an experiment proves that they don't have a charism because the test was a big, fat zero. They try to use the gift, but their efforts neither penetrate the situation nor other people's awareness with any real effect. No one notices. Nothing happens. If this describes you, you know how disheartening it can be. It's tempting to jettison the whole process and tell yourself it's all a bunch of bunk. Please don't. There are some good reasons your experience was a goose egg, and it's worth finding out what they are.

Have you come to this process looking for more than discernment? We have all had points in our lives when we felt isolated and lonely, longing to be seen and heard by others. Some of us were attracted to the process of discerning spiritual gifts after having lost a job, or a spouse; we came not so much out of readiness to unfold new meaning in our lives, but more because we wanted a weapon to combat our hurt. Feeling gifted can give you proof that you're lovable, powerful, worthy, or even that life itself is worthwhile. However, when you've got your heart set on a specific charism

---

[26] *Meditations and Devotions*

41

for that "proof," you will not allow yourself to see the situation accurately. If you find yourself in this situation as you're discerning a gift, there are several things you can do to take your discernment deeper:

- Firstly, accept your own limitations and need-related motives for beginning this process. Christ said, "It is not the healthy who need the doctor, but the sick" (Matthew 9:12). Accepting these limits may require quite a bit of prayer, and you may find confiding in your priest, a spiritual director, counselor, or a good friend who listens well very helpful. Some great Scripture passages to soak in include The Blind Bartimaeus (Mark 10:46-52), The Woman with the Hemorrhage (Mark 5:25-34), and The Poor Widow's Contribution (Mark 12:41-44).

- Consider how prone you may be to overlook positive evidence. Some people, often men, put very little stock in their feelings. If you tend to consider your feelings irrelevant, you may find it hard to recognize the inner experience of a charism. Also, if you are feeling depressed, are apt to expect the worst from events, or tend toward self-depreciative thinking, you may overlook positive results. And if you are struggling with your relationships, getting feedback may be tricky. You may have to take some risks and be willing to offer what you have to give, regardless of your rapport with any one person. The charisms operate independent of our own human frailties; they are so compelling people will often respond regardless of how close you are to them personally.

- Above all, *suspend your judgment!* You need more time and experiences before you can make any definitive statements about your gifts. Pay special attention to the points mentioned already about apparent contradiction, and *listen* to the evidence people in your discernment group notice when you describe your experience. You may also consider talking further with a veteran Siena-trained Interviewer.

> **If you did not experiment, or if you resist continuing**
>
> Take enough prayerful time to check-in with yourself. *Something* attracted you to extended discernment; something *else* is holding you back. It may simply be time conflicts or other demands that have to be dealt with. But are there are also fears, unmet needs, and unbearable hopes that may cause you to procrastinate, resist experimenting, or jump to conclusions? And are you, therefore, avoiding authentic testing in certain situations? There are two things to be said. One: perhaps this is not a good time to discern. It takes a certain amount of inner freedom to be able to look for patterns of giftedness in your life and experiment to clarify them. It's okay to focus on the healing you need and come back to this later. Two: attending to such matters is also part of answering God's call. Understanding your needs, longings, and resistances is a vital step in discovering the "true name" he has given you to which your charisms point. He is with you when you look into that dark mirror.

III) Apparent confusion: What to do with strongly mixed signals

What if the evidence is so motley, you aren't even clear enough to muster *doubt?* Being in a place of confusion during this process is an *excellent* sign. It means you are watching carefully what happens when you use a gift—the single most important

42

element in successful discernment. Rest assured that as long as you keep testing and watching, you will come to know your charisms.

Apparent confusion is the most common frustration for people who are discerning the thread of a charism from a great bundle of experience. Everyone, however, may find themselves confused as they step from an early, superficial conclusion about the presence or absence of a charism into deeper discernment. For example, if you were initially assuming that the charism was doubtful, upon reflection you may now see aspects of some situations you were overlooking that seem to support the presence of a charism.

Attempts at using a charism can lead to confusion if one of the three signs remains stubbornly inconsistent from one experience to the next. Your inner experience may find you with mixed feelings. The actual effectiveness may be real, but resist efforts to form a pattern. Then, of course, other people's responses may be mixed. You would have a hard time, therefore, reaching consensus about it one way or the other.

It's important to note that *individual* attempts to exercise a charism often yield mixed signals, especially as experience with the discernment process causes you to put less stock in your personal feelings about what happened, and more in actual results and others' responses. Apparent confusion is not all that telling with only individual experiences under our belt. It does, however, become an issue to the extent that it continues over an *extended* period of time and doesn't clear up with experimentation. Further testing is a must for anyone in this situation; but it truly needs to be *targeted*. Let's look at the three possibilities.

Your inner experience varies from one situation to another

In this case, for example, you seem to be very effective when you use the gift, and other people give you positive feedback, but you often find the activity tiring, draining, and unconnected to your spiritual life. Here, it's important not to just chalk up those feelings to selfishness and shrug them off. Christians are called to endure suffering, but never as an end in itself![27] Christ wasn't kidding when he said his yoke was easy and his burden light. Charisms are meant to be life-giving to their bearers as well as their recipients. If you haven't experienced this energizing quality many of the times you've engaged in this activity, chances are good that something else is fueling the other two signs—your consistent effectiveness and positive feedback. It could be a natural ability, or it could be a different charism at work.

■ **Try making a list of the experiences you've had related to this charism, and then go through them looking for any patterns in your inner experiences.** Which aspect of the activity don't you enjoy? Which *do* you? Is there another charism that's similar and may account for the part you do enjoy? (Check the *Key* in back for these details.) For example, if you delight in bringing order from chaos but find delegating and coordinating the work of others tiresome, you may be looking at Wisdom instead of Administration. In these cases, you need to target your experiments to test between the two charisms so you can clarify what you're actually doing.

---

[27] For more on the Church's teachings on this subject, see the Siena audio series *The Call to Christian Happiness.*

■ Is there a pattern in the situations you didn't enjoy that shows your inner experience of using this gift was dependent on certain circumstances? For example, was your energy level contingent on involvement with a certain person, or a certain outcome? This could be a clue that a charism of Helps is also in the picture, which itself would need to be tested and verified by all three signs. However, it could also mean you had a personal need, such as recognition, that was involved, which does not rule out the presence of the charism, but does make it more difficult to detect. The challenge will be to try to satisfy the personal need in a different way, and then focus your discernment heavily on the actual results of your efforts to engage in the charism-activity.

Focusing on the Feeling

What if you really enjoy the activity consistently—it feels like "home"—but you honestly can't say it's prayerful or connected to your relationship with God? There are two possibilities. One is that a well-developed natural ability is involved, not a charism. But another is that it simply may never have occurred to you to picture this activity as having anything to do with God. We have met a number of Catholics who find it hard to imagine their work or involvements outside the parish as related to their faith in any significant way. Praying a rosary is spiritual, running a meeting at work or coaching a softball team is not. Such things are too earthy. If this tendency is true of you, then taking a moment to pray before engaging in this activity is probably a new experience for you. You will not have spent much time considering the spiritual meaning of what you have been doing. Understanding for the first time what your faith may have to do with your work or play is exciting, but it can make discerning between a charism and a natural talent or acquired skill more complicated.

How do you tell the difference? You can experience a significant qualitative difference between the underlying *joy* of using a spiritual gift and the *enjoyment* of engaging a natural talent or acquired skill you do well. The enjoyment that comes from natural facility is mainly characterized by a sense of *satisfaction*, of prevailing over the challenges of the situation. Why? Because you're running on your own power and the achievement is something you have earned yourself. There is that victorious "*Yessss!*" you experience, like doing a little touchdown dance on the inside.

With a spiritual gift, however, the dominant experience is not one of pride and achievement, but of wonder, gratitude, and *participation* in something far beyond what you could personally achieve. The joy felt in using a charism has a freshness, a delight to it that focuses us outside ourselves and our efforts. It isn't always exuberant; it may be quite subtle. But it is always buoyant, raising us out of ourselves. This happens whenever we encounter something that pulls us up short in surprise and wonder (though individuals may be more or less aware of it). It's how we respond to something exquisitely beautiful, for example, like a piece of music that brings tears to our eyes. We experience it when we suddenly understand the truth about something or someone. It's there when we notice how good something is, such as when we're thirsty and drink a tall glass of water. We feel it when we recognize the oneness of things: when two friends find themselves in simpatico, for example, or when we recognize a meaningful pattern in a quagmire of details. Joy is an experience of participating in something wonderful beyond our expectations, something we know to be truly vital, truly significant. And because it takes us outside ourselves, it comes

44

hand-in-hand with humility, that awareness of the excellence of our own littleness in relation to our Creator. A charism will be marked by this continuing sense of privilege.

If you realize you seem to be enjoying a natural ability but not the true supernatural joy of a spiritual gift, yet the other two signs still point compellingly toward a charism, try looking at whether the talent or skill you're using is acting as a launch pad for a different charism. For instance, the *natural* love of learning and information-gathering you first thought was Knowledge could be the platform from which a supernatural gift of Evangelism does its work. Again, you'll need to look for the pattern, identify another potential charism, and adjust your experiments to clarify what's happening.

My experiments do not consistently meet with success

When your inner experience seems to point strongly toward a charism, but your actual effectiveness is all over the board, there are three possibilities. One is that it's really another charism at work. A second is that you do have this charism, but it is aimed at certain kinds of situations. And a third is that this charism is being modified by another charism. For example, an Encourager/Intercessor experiences a strong call and is particularly effective when praying for specific individuals. On the other hand, Intercessors who also have a charism of Leadership may find themselves especially effective when praying for the mission, work, and people of the organizations they lead.

Again, you need to list all your experiences with this gift and look for any patterns where you *were* effective. How did the situations differ between the ineffective times and those that were a success? Were circumstances vastly different? Were you with different kinds of people? People with different needs? And what exactly did you *do* to use the gift? Did you do anything differently when your efforts were a clear success than when they were not?

Sometimes noticing what was different in what you actually did between your success and failures will simultaneously reveal that you probably do not have one charism, but are actually using another. When Sherry Weddell first started working with people concerned with their spiritual growth, her positive one-on-one experiences led her to believe she might have the charism of Encouragement. And yet she consistently experienced only mediocre results nurturing those who came to her with emotional needs. By looking at what kinds of people she did seem to succeed in helping—individuals seeking clarity and perspective rather than healing and personal nurture—she realized she was working instead with the charism of Wisdom mixed in with some well-practiced listening skills. She was effective with those who needed insight and help solving problems, but not with those who primarily needed comfort and emotional support.

Feedback isn't always confirming

If your successfulness seems to correlate with the people you were with, it may be a feedback problem. Feedback is often inconsistently helpful when experimenting with a charism simply because there are so many factors that can account for it. The most notable factor is the level of awareness and expressiveness of the people with whom you used the gift. Just keep in mind that the main thing to look for is recurring indifference or merely polite acknowledgement from people *over a significant period of time.*

Again, the most helpful question to ask is where you seemed to be effective. Is there a pattern? Who seemed to be receiving the gift in those situations? How are they similar to each other? How are they different from those who were involved when you weren't effective?

Charisms are never generic. They work within the context of your personality, your life experience, the needs of your community, and your other charisms. The charism of Leadership, for example, won't empower you to pick up the reins in just any situation—it makes you effective in an area in which you have vision. Likewise, the charism of Missionary isn't simply a passport to hurdle you over every cross-cultural barrier; it attracts you to a particular culture and empowers you to carry on successfully within it. It may be that the charism you are discerning is similarly focused on a specific group.

You will need to experiment further, though, to make sure of this, and to eliminate the possibility that it might not be a different charism altogether. You do that by looking at what you were actually *doing* in the successful situations (see the section above on inconsistent results). You may be effective at teaching children, for example, because you're actually providing the *encouragement* they need to learn. You'll want to look at the descriptions of both charisms again and decide what the heart of it is for you. Is it one or the other? Or both?

Finally, indirect feedback you've overlooked may account for your mixed results. If people keep coming back to you for advice or ideas, don't ignore that evidence simply because no one has directly commented on how wise your insights prove to be. Body language and facial expressions are legitimate forms of feedback, too. And when you're confused, don't forget you can usually *ask* people what they receive through you! This can shed much light on confusing results.

IV) Apparent confirmation: your experience reveals a probable charism

This is the most fun place to find yourself in during the discernment process: hot on the scent of a spiritual gift! You may have only just begun exploring this aptitude and have had one or two successful experiences. Or, if you've had considerable practice with the activity already, you may have just recognized a significant incident that reaffirmed and illuminated a whole line of similar experiences that together satisfy the three signs of the charism. Both are great places to be: they tell you you're headed in the right direction.

If your experience is somewhat limited, we want to encourage you to remain tentative yet. Success is very exciting and will tempt you to make final conclusions about the presence of this gift. But we have observed a common developmental process you should know about. Often those who assume they have a gift after a few experiments are later struck by real doubt that they have the gift. This doubt can arise because they were not discerning *deeply*, but focusing mainly on positive evidence without asking enough questions. When circumstances later raise questions, they come as a shock. Such a shock can be harsh enough that people jump to the opposite conclusion: they were fooling themselves and don't have the charism at all. You can avoid these extremes by putting off judgment for six months of active experimentation, and in the meantime questioning the charism and testing it. As we mentioned above, a little doubt is excellent for thorough discernment.

If you already have accumulated a lot of experience, however, you can take your discernment deeper by looking closely at the patterns that are evident.

> ## What a true 'yes' looks like
>
> Real confidence in a charism comes from watching a pattern of evidence come into ever-clearer focus over months and even years, evidence that has withstood doubts and many tests. It includes a very firm understanding of the charism—how it works, what it does, how it is distinct from other spiritual gifts and natural abilities. Such a pattern shows the charism working in spite of the personal frailties and mistakes made while trying to use it. Only experience with using the gift, and careful attention to what happens when you do, can justify such confidence.

■ **Make a list of the actual events that form the chain of experience with this gift.** Note why you think each is connected to this particular charism. Use the *Key to the Charisms* in the back to check what you've noted against the facts we've provided about this particular charism and its signs. Hold that measuring stick against each of your experiences. As your understanding of the charism grows, keep experimenting and watching.

■ **Up the ante as you gain confidence. Explore how the gift works in different settings and with different people.** For example, if you're fairly certain you have the charism of Mercy, sit down and list as many times as you can remember when you have been a powerful channel of God's love through practical acts of compassion. Note what it was about each incident that made you think the charism of Mercy was operating (beyond the normal Christian virtue). Check the *Key*. Now, how could you up the ante? Where could you go to relieve *greater* pain within the particular kind of suffering to which you seem to be called? If it's terminal illness, can you work with strangers in a hospice as effectively as you have with people in your church? If it's depression, can you expand your sphere from informal personal relationships with family members and friends to more formal ones, perhaps extending practical compassion to people you work with?

This final step—expanding your reach with the charism while taking more risks—is essential. It is what allows the gift to show its truly supernatural effectiveness and do its work. It is what allows the larger path of your *vocation*—to which all of your charisms, skills, and talents point—to become visible. And it is what allows each of us to grow in faith, integrity, humility and spiritual strength so we can live out that marvelous collaborative work as brothers and sisters of Christ.[28] Take a few minutes now and use what you've just learned to adjust your experiment and take your discernment efforts deeper. Let's dig out the pattern that lies in your experiences.

---

[28] See the article on Baptism and Confirmation in *Additional Helps* (appendix) for more on our privileged role as Christians.

Something to try: **Delight thankfully in the privilege**

When you do feel that you've truly experienced one of your charisms in action, make sure you take time with God to celebrate this magnificent event. You truly have experienced a grace-filled moment.

Think about what you have just participated in. While you were using the gift—in those moments, you were sharing personally in God's work to save his people (Note the charisms are directed to the service of the *whole* human family because Christ died to redeem all people). To get a living sense of what this means try this: Thinking about how you just used a charism, imagine the Lord Jesus standing next to you, putting his arm around your shoulders, turning you toward that situation, the people, the need you perceived, and saying:

See, this is how I...

Administration: *coordinate things with perfect economy and smooth the way for my people*
Celibacy: *befriend those I love in total freedom*
Craftsmanship: *give physical form to what is beautiful, good, and true through the creativity of my people*
Discernment of Spirits: *see and address the influence of spirits on my people*
Encouragement: *hearten and counsel my discouraged ones*
Evangelism: *bring the Good News of Salvation to each person*
Faith: *remind my people to expect great things of God*
Giving: *pour out my infinite riches on my people*
Healing: *restore each of my broken, injured ones to wholeness and well-being*
Helps: *amplify the good work of those who serve me*
Hospitality: *see my lonely ones and welcome them*
Intercessory Prayer: *direct the Father's blessings and provision to those I love through prayer on their behalf*

Knowledge: *see the goodness of all Creation and delight in the truth it reveals about the One who holds all things together in being*
Leadership: *lead my people out of bondage and into freedom to build the Kingdom of God*
Mercy: *comfort those who suffer*
Missionary: *delight in all peoples and cultures*
Music: *call to the hearts of my people through the truth and beauty of sound*
Pastoring: *gather my people together and make them strong in spirit*
Prophecy: *speak directly and compellingly to my people*
Service: *go about meeting the needs of those I love*
Teaching: *provide and present the knowledge and skills my people need to grow*
Voluntary Poverty: *empower my disciples to imitate me and serve the poor*
Wisdom: *illuminate situations and guide my people to realize the Good*
Writing: *reveal myself and nurture my people through words of truth and beauty*

Using a charism is like opening a window through which you see a sliver of how things are done in the Kingdom of Heaven. In a very real way, it is the Lord sharing himself personally with you as he goes about redeeming the world. There is only one appropriate response to this: profound gratitude celebrated with amazed delight!

Quarry the pattern buried in your experiences

List five significant incidents in which you think you may have used the charism you are exploring. Then survey each experience for evidence of the three signs. Put a plus under the signs that gave positive evidence of the charism, a minus under signs that pointed away from the charism, and a question mark where you were not sure what the sign was telling you or where you haven't received enough information yet to evaluate the sign. (If you need help thinking through the incidents in detail, use the questions in this session's reflection on pages 52-53)

Charism:

Incident	Inner Experience	Actual Effectiveness	Others' response
1.			
2.			
3.			
4.			
5.			

Do you see a pattern among the signs? Where do you have positive evidence? Negative? Where was the sign inconclusive? Is there a predominance of any of these? Which incidents break the pattern?

Based on what you see, do you need to suspend or come to judgement? How many question marks did you have? Five or more is a strong indication you need to suspend your judgement and gain more experience. How many incidents were you able to list where you truly attempted to use the charism in question as it's meant to be used? If you were only able to fill in two or three, you again need more experience.

Considering the whole list above, not an individual incident, which of the four situations best describes your relationship now with the charism you're exploring?

❑ Apparent contradiction—evidence seems to cast doubt on the charism

❑ Apparent zero—there is no evidence either for or against the charism

❑ Apparent confusion—evidence seems to confirm or contradict depending on the situation

❑ Apparent confirmation—the evidence seems to point to presence of the charism

In what particular area(s) do you need to explore further to gain a clearer sense of whether you have this charism? What could you do, especially in the next two weeks, to gain additional experience that is likely to shed light on these specific areas?

Go back to the section on the topic you just checked. Write down as many ideas as you can think of. Keep in mind whether your objective is to suspend judgment, or discern more clearly. If you get stuck, note any questions you want to clarify within your group discussion.

Discerning Together: Help each other go deeper

A small group of fellow discerners can be a *big* help when it comes to asking and answering the kinds of questions we've been raising in this chapter. This second meeting should be a place both to get support and give it; often it can be easier to see evidence and patterns of charisms in someone else's experience, which we see objectively, than it can be when we look at our own. Everyone will get the most out of the gathering if each person strives for two things: to share his or her experience exploring a charism in enough detail to allow other people to say what they hear and see in it, and to listen helpfully to the reports of others.

What does "helpful" listening entail? It depends on who is talking! If it is someone with limited experience, a sensitive personality, or anyone facing a significant revision in how she sees herself, helpful listening means encouraging the person, recognizing what she may be feeling, and pointing out whatever evidence you can that will help her *suspend* judgement. If it is a mature discerner who shows resilience, has a lot of experience with the activity, and indicates a real desire to get to the bottom of it, helpful listening may entail asking more pointed questions. They need to find in all that enthusiasm and experience what is truly relevant to the charism in question. To really help means you'll need to make sure that you're familiar with the charism and its signs.

When it's your turn to share your experiences with the group, focus on describing what happened and then asking for whatever it is you need from the group. Ask questions if you're confused—you're probably not the only one. It's just as okay to tell how excited you are at your successes as it is to complain about your frustrations and disappointments so far. That's what this group is for. Tap their wisdom and understanding.

Also, don't forget the ground rules: protect each other's confidence, stick with discernment, voice your needs, share insights carefully, and let people discern for themselves: never tell anyone they do or do not have a charism.

When listening to each person, ask yourself:

- Where are they in the discernment process? Are they in a place of apparent contradiction? Confusion? Confirmation? Are they just dead in the water?

- Do they need to *suspend* or *come to* judgement? Sometimes people have difficulty accurately gauging this need themselves. Do you sense that they need to take it more gently? Or push a little harder?

- Is there anything they've overlooked? Any evidence of the charism they've missed? Any pattern pieces they aren't seeing? Any areas they need to test further? Any ways to adjust their experiments that they may not have considered?

- How can I point out what I see with tact and wisdom?

Discussion Questions

Spend a few minutes as a group organizing your thoughts on the discussion questions privately. You may want to glance back through the personal reflection you completed at the beginning of this chapter, as well as the pattern worksheet. Then, take the next hour and a half to give each person time to share what they want to of their answers to the questions. Go around the table once—listening to each person's full report before moving on to the next. *Do not interrupt*; take notes if you want to point something out that you've noticed in the experiences of others. Once each person has finished telling his or her story, the group can offer its insights, suggestions, and encouragement. However, have someone designated as time-checker to keep the discussion moving around the whole table. Every person must get a chance to report and receive some feedback. Lengthy responses and more complex discussion should be tabled until everyone has had their turn.

What charism are you discerning? Describe the significant incident you explored in the reflection on page 34.

What happened when you engaged in the activity? Which signs were apparent?

What is your current sense of this charism concerning the four possible scenarios discussed above? Does the evidence seem to cast doubt on the charism? Is there little evidence either for or against the charism? Does the evidence seem to confirm sometimes and contradict others? Or does it seems to point to the presence of the charism? Why?

Do you see any patterns yet in your experiences with this activity?

Is there any area you're having trouble discerning at this point?

What do you plan to do to deepen your discernment? How will you adjust your experiment?

Closing prayer

Once everyone has had a chance to share, go around the table once more and ask—like last time—how each person would like the other members of the group to pray for them until you gather again in two weeks. Note each other's requests. When you're finished, pray together. Thank God for what people have shared, ask for his blessing—especially the gifts of faith and courage. You may want to close the session by saying together the prayer of Thomas Merton given below.

53

Between now and the final session, put into action one or two of your ideas to adjust your experiments. See if you can take one new risk with this gift that might allow it to do its work more powerfully. In the final section, we will look into what we can do to get out of the way of our spiritual gifts.

O Lord God, I have no idea where I am going.
I do not see the road ahead of me.
I cannot know for certain where it will end.
Nor do I really know myself, and the fact that I think I am following Your will does not mean that I am actually doing so.

But I do believe that the desire to please you does in fact please you.
I hope I have that desire in all that I am doing... that I will never do anything apart from that desire. I know that if I do this, You will lead me by the right road though I may know nothing about it.
Therefore, I will trust you always though I may seem to be lost...I will not fear, for You are ever with me, and You will never leave me to face my perils alone.

Session 3: Getting out of the way

You have learned how to effectively plan and carry out experiments to explore the charism you chose. You have also seen how to avoid making flawed judgments about its presence in your life by pushing into deeper experimentation and allowing the evidence to accumulate into a pattern. Unfocused experiments and hasty conclusions are two of the road hazards most likely to run your discernment efforts into the ditch. There is a third, however, that is perhaps the subtlest obstacle to recognizing and using spiritual gifts. It is *our own tendency to get in their way*. Before this guided tour of the discernment process is done, we would like you to experience what happens when you consciously remove impediments and let a charism work freely.

How we hinder our charisms

As we experiment with our charisms and watch what happens, we are likely to discover that we possess *habits of thinking and acting* that hinder their effectiveness. Many of these habits are unconscious strategies that we learned as children for controlling life and dealing with fear. They may no longer be suitable now that we are adults, and may actually prevent us from using our charisms successfully. Why? Because our unconscious coping strategies usually encourage us to use charisms to meet our *own* needs. As we attempt to act through the gift to serve someone else, we simultaneously try to obtain something for ourselves, usually without even realizing it.

For example, let's say that there is real evidence that Barbara has a charism of Service. She is regularly drawn by the Holy Spirit to personally fill gaps and solve problems so that good things can happen in her community. But she also has a deep unsatisfied need to be recognized by others. She may find herself using her charism to *earn people's gratitude* or *recognition* and feel hurt when her contribution goes unnoticed, even though someone with the charism of Service usually prefers to remain behind the scenes. This attention-seeking could undermine her confidence in the charism since the emotional turmoil that she experiences after using the gift would seem to contradict what the inner experience of Service should feel like. Also, her hurt feelings may make it difficult for those whom she serves to receive the gift because they feel guilty or resentful.

Or another example: Ray has a charism of Knowledge. He is led by the Holy Spirit to study and contemplate human nature, the business world, and Sacred Scripture, and to share the truths he discovers with others. Simultaneously, though, Ray also seeks *to be the expert*. He may find himself using his gift to attract people's esteem. Gradually, he begins focusing on what people think *of him* instead of what knowledge of the truth will do *for them*. Especially if he starts coming off as a self-absorbed know-it-all, his attempts to use the charism will become less and less effective.

When we try to use the charisms of the Holy Spirit to meet our own needs this way, it's like levying a little tax on the good we're delivering; it makes the whole process more emotionally expensive for everyone. Fortunately, Jesus is a known companion of tax collectors! Over time, we can learn to pass on the whole gift of love that God is empowering us to deliver with few or no strings attached. And as we grow in this discipline of detachment, we will become less driven by anxiety and compulsivity.

Getting out of the way is as normal a part of developing charisms as is experimenting and watching for the three signs. Most of us, at one point or another, want to achieve something for ourselves in our use of a spiritual gift in addition to serving God and our neighbor. We bring expectations to the experience—hopes for recognition, for friendship, for relief from our own doubts or suffering, even something as tangible as a better job and salary. In fact, it is not at all uncommon for people to be drawn to gifts discernment because they are unhappy with their current life or career situation.

Please note, however, that this dissatisfaction is a perfectly legitimate reason to begin discerning your charisms and vocational call. In fact, it implies something marvelous: at least part of you really believes that God means you to be happy in this life, and that you can discover what that happiness entails. It is wonderful to realize that such faith and love of God reside inside us! However, the desire to obtain a better life, a better job, or better relationships must be consciously separated from our efforts to take up a charism in the service of others. Why? Because detaching the use of our charisms from the process of meeting our real human needs gives us:

❑ Greater access to the inner experience of peace and joy that comes with using a charism
❑ More powerful effectiveness with the gift as we open the door wider to God
❑ A more radiant impact on the hearts of those who receive the goods of the charism

Obviously, all of these make discernment easier, allowing the evidence of the three signs to shine with much brighter wattage. Before we take a quick look at how this happens, we should briefly consider an area of confusion that can color what we expect from using a charism: the relationship between charisms and our vocation.

Discerning and using a charism ≠ discerning a vocation

Discerning a charism does not equal discerning a vocation. The relationship between spiritual gifts and vocation is very real, but it is not as direct as people often assume it to be. While your charisms are clues to your vocation, they do not *necessitate* a particular life. A charism by itself calls you to one thing: **simply to give the gift itself away.** We can be drawn to pray for others without having a call to become a Carmelite;[29] to organize a group event without pursuing a career as a CEO; and to offer guidance and insight to someone facing a serious dilemma even though we have no intention of becoming a professional counselor. The circumstances under which we can best give our gifts vary dramatically from person to person, sometimes even from period to period in one person's life, depending on God's will for each of us.

Using our charisms helps us move toward that purpose by setting events in motion, by creating opportunities for the recognition and support of others to reach us, by teaching us about ourselves and about God, and by schooling us in being open and responsive to the promptings of the Holy Spirit. But during the time we use a gift, we must set aside past and future and embrace the "obedience of the present

---

[29] The Carmelite Order is an ancient Catholic religious order particularly devoted to contemplation, penance, and prayer for others. Some of the greatest Christian mystics in history such as St. Teresa of Avila, St. John of the Cross, and St. Therese of Lisieux were Carmelites.

moment."[30] All we should seek when we're using a charism—and all we can expect—is that *God will touch <u>this</u> person or <u>this</u> situation through our gift*. Leaders will successfully communicate a vision and engage others in changing our world for the better. God's purposes will be accomplished and his provision will reach those in need through the prayer of Intercessors. Those with a charism of Celibacy will remain cheerfully free of romantic involvements while rejoicing in deep friendships. We can count on God entering the situation through the gifts he has bestowed on us if we're open, but we cannot control *how*. We're speaking of God, remember, "whose foolishness is wiser than the wisdom of men."[31] We do not know and cannot anticipate exactly what he will do through this charism for this person in this situation.

> *What we can and should do is fix our attention on how the charism is doing its specific work and how good it is to be here.*

When a person uses a charism of Music, therefore, he can expect to translate the beauty and truth of human experience and potential into sound. He can expect to perform well. And he can expect God to do something wonderful through the music he creates. These are the basic goods of the charism. What he cannot expect is that everyone in his audience will like him, or that people he doesn't know will invite him over for dinner. Nor can he assume that God intends him to quit his day job. These things may indeed happen. They may be part of God's purpose for his life. However, they are only incidental to the use of this charism in this moment for the sake of others. The inner joy and energy of using a charism, and the positive impact it has on others will be present over time, but we simply cannot anticipate how we will feel or what others will experience in any given situation. Over time, our gifted musician *will* help others experience delight and thanksgiving through his music. But during any given performance, he cannot ensure that they have some particular experience, nor can he count on feeling joy and well-being himself.

We should mention an important point at this juncture: Having imperfect motives does *not* rule out the presence of a charism! God's mercy is boundless; he will leverage whatever morsel of good will we possess and lead us to wholeness, no matter what else may motivate us at the beginning. As St. Paul says, "Where there was sin, there grace abounded even more" (Romans 5:20b). *Examining the ways we "tax" our charisms is not about judging whether we are good or bad.* It is simply about discerning the barriers that keep us from using our charisms more effectively. Jesus himself said, "I did not come to condemn the world, but to save the world."[32]

Whenever we find ourselves looking for a particular outcome in addition to the charism's normal impact, it's a sure sign we're saddling the gift with our own

---

[30] As Uncle Screwtape (a demon) tells his nephew while teaching him the habits of being a highly effective hellion: *"The humans live in time but the Enemy* (Screwtape's name for God) *destines them to eternity. He therefore, I believe, wants them to attend chiefly to two things: to eternity itself, and to that point of time which they call the Present. For the Present is the point at which time touches eternity. . .in it alone freedom and actuality are offered them. He would therefore have them continually concerned either with eternity (which means being concerned with Him) or with the Present. . .obeying the present voice of conscience, bearing the present cross, receiving the present grace, giving thanks for the present pleasure." (C. S. Lewis, The Screwtape Letters, Macmillan, 1948, p.76-77.)*

[31] *1 Corinthians 1:25*
[32] *John 12:47*

expectations. We can and should fix our attention instead on what God is doing, letting ourselves respond like St. Peter who, with James and John, when he saw Christ revealed in his Divine glory at the Transfiguration,[33] exclaimed, *"Lord! It is good that we are here!"* Focusing on what *is* happening (instead of what we hoped would happen) cultivates attentive wonder at what God is doing for his people, and for ourselves. Wonder brings joy and releases us from self-interest like nothing else; it's key to getting out of the way.

Mixed motives confuse our inner experience of a charism

On the other hand, to the extent that we try to exercise a charism solely as a way to achieve personal happiness, overcome depression, or win friends and influence people, we end up frustrated. Charisms wither when diverted from their purpose of bearing God's love to others. This hijacking is often painfully evident in our inner experience of using the gift. Unconsciously looking to meet our own needs usually stirs up a bubbling stew of anxious feelings that muddle the inner joy and peace we normally feel when the Holy Spirit works through us.

We can go into a situation anticipating that we'll do something we can feel good about. We'll see someone become happier, more peaceful, empowered, or whole thanks to our efforts. And we'll know because they will be glad we were there. But what if it doesn't work out this way—when there is evidence that someone was comforted, or empowered, or healed, and they walk out the door oblivious to our role in it? Our thoughts and emotions can take a nose dive. We may be hurt, disappointed, even angry, resenting the person's ingratitude. We may confuse their lack of response to us personally with a lack of response to the charism and doubt that we have the gift. In fact, any of the feelings we experience when we don't get what we need or want are likely to rise up and mask the energizing, vital purposefulness we normally would feel using the charism.

Mixed motives blunt our effectiveness

The actual ability of the charism to achieve its effect can also be hindered when we use it for our own ends. Participants in our discernment workshops sometimes ask if they can hurt someone in the process of exploring and using their charisms. The answer is: it's possible—in the absence of love. People who have a basic sensitivity and respect for the freedom of others rarely hurt others when experimenting with their charisms. For instance, mature people exploring Wisdom don't demand that others take their advice. Savvy Discerners keep their perceptions confidential. Detached Prophets don't try to control responses to the words they share, and loving Administrators don't impose a harsh order on others.

As long as we are gentle and don't try to control people's responses, as long as we recognize their freedom to accept or reject the gift and truly let them encounter the Holy Spirit, we won't hurt people. Even if the results of our experimentation make it clear that we don't have a charism in a particular area, no harm will be done. None of us loves perfectly and we will all make mistakes as we discern. But our mistakes will seldom, if ever, harm another if we keep our attention focused upon the ultimate goal: the good of those we seek to serve and God's purposes for them. But the more driven we are, the more likely we are to run roughshod over the rightful boundaries

---

[33] See *Matthew 17: 1-8; Mark 9:1-8*

58

of others in pursuit of our personal agenda. "Let go and let God" is an excellent rule for those engaged in the discernment of charisms.

Mixed motives make it difficult for others to receive God's love

We've all had the experience of someone offering to help us, only to find out that there was a price. Maybe it was a relative who bought an expensive birthday present for you and then gave you the silent treatment when you only sent a card for Christmas. Perhaps it was a coworker who offered to stay late to help you finish part of a project and then expected you to listen sympathetically to a half-hour long litany of grievances against the company. Resentment is the natural response when others volunteer to give and then expect us to pay.

Putting a price tag on a charism, which is a vehicle of unconditional love, can really dampen others people's ability to receive the goods of the charism. When we expect to get something from others in return for using a charism, we are often disappointed and it usually shows. Our hurt feelings, anger, frustration, or melancholy can make people feel guilty about impinging on us. This effect defeats the whole purpose of a charism, which is to deliver God's love and provision to others. People may fear to anger or upset us in the future. They may feel manipulated. They may decide *it's not worth the price* to receive our Help, our Wisdom, our Service, our Teaching, our Craftsmanship, our Giving.

Finally, not only can personal agenda sour our inner experience of the charism, injure our actual effectiveness, and dampen other people's ability to receive the gift, they also prevent us from getting our needs met properly in the way God intended: through the love and charisms of others. If we're busy quieting our needs with the tidbits of attention, gratitude, respect and affection we skim from our efforts to serve others, we can avoid having to admit our true needs for and dependence upon others. We never give them the chance to help us. Our ulterior motives, therefore, not only keep our own charisms from achieving their full effectiveness, they can hinder other people's charisms from reaching *us*!

With so many ways self-interest can confound the work of our charisms, it's obvious we need to get out of the way. In fact, the process can become so frustrating and painful if we *don't*, that we're likely to give up discerning our charisms altogether. But what can we do if most of this happens automatically, despite our best intentions? We can become aware of our underlying needs and the strategies we've developed to cope with them, and we can make the courageous act of releasing our chokehold on control. It isn't easy, but it is fairly simple. There may be as many ways to get in the way of a charism as there are human needs, but they all sprout from the same cause: fear.

Fear: the Heart of mixed motives

Everywhere that the Siena Institute has offered the *Called & Gifted Program*, participants report that fear is the single biggest problem with discerning charisms. Some fear there might really be something to this idea of vocation. Discernment affirms our deep hope that our own life has special meaning. When that hope is raised from the depths, we hardly dare entertain it—it's too good to be true. Other people are afraid that they do have a call, but that they won't get it right. Somehow, they will miss the purpose of their life. For some, it's the prospect of releasing control of their lives—of possibly being called to something other than what they want for themselves—that makes their hearts quail. And still other people blanch at the

59

thought of taking responsibility, of accepting just how much what they do with their life matters.

Then there are the fears attached to the process of exploring gifts: of taking risks to serve others, of failing, or making fools of ourselves, of not being humble enough, of hurting others, and especially of consequences. At some level, we may worry about how using a charism will alter the roles we play in our relationships and how it will challenge the unwritten rules of the groups we belong to.

Finally, and deepest of all, there is the fear of deprivation. The fear of scarcity—that our innate needs will not be met. We need to be loved. We need to be valued. We need others to confirm our goodness. We need to be safe. Each of us needs to be effective, to be able to do some things well. We need our efforts to be encouraged and recognized by others. We need to grow. And we need to be able to rest, really rest. These needs are good; the Lord made us this way.

It's not our needs, therefore, that cause problems. It's rather what we do out of our *fear they won't be met.* When we scramble out of fear to meet them in the wrong way, we can hurt our relationship to God and to others. When charisms are bent to

Fear of Deprivation: the queen of worries

Everything that causes us fear in the discernment process stems from a basic anxiety that we won't receive what we need. Why do we worry about failing when we try to use a charism? Because it might cost us the affirmation we need from others. Why are we afraid we might miss our vocation? Because we fear we won't have the virtue and good will to see and do what we need to.

But fear of deprivation, and all the worry it spawns, is based on a big, fat fallacy: the assumption that *we have to provide for ourselves.* Fear whispers to us, "You'd better look out for number one; no one else is going to." Life tends to reinforce this fallacy. We've all been deprived of something we needed deeply at one time or another. And we learn at a young age to take matters into our own hands, to maneuver to protect our self-interest. But in doing this, we take on a burden we cannot possibly carry successfully. We *do* depend on others. We cannot satisfy our own need for love. We cannot simply "love ourselves." Nor can we make others love us. When we try, we can at best maneuver people into giving us what *looks* like love. But instead of fulfilled, we end up anxious. Because we have attempted to engineer the situation, we doubt it's authenticity and how long it will last. This is true even when someone truly does love us—the more we've tried to attain it, the less we tend to trust it. All because **we're trying to exert a control over situations and people we simply do not have.**

The entire history of God's people and the very abundance of creation joyously testify against the *lie* that scarcity is reality and that we must provide for ourselves. Although we do take active responsibility for our needs, it is active *receiving,* not generating. Even when you work hard to put a roof over your head, you continually benefit from the labor and gifts of many other people—the job created by some entrepreneur, the education you received from teachers, the life received from your parents, even the lumber for your home was cut and milled by others. It is God's providence that reaches us through these intermediaries. But we're not limited to what we can get through other people. Not only does God provide material to satisfy our physical needs, he provides grace and salvation, and invites each of us into a direct relationship with him.

Which means…*we have nothing to fear* (though the process by which we learn this may be a long one!). Throughout Scripture, we are reminded not to be afraid more than 365 times—enough for every day of the year! Many of these reminders show God meeting our most *basic* needs: clothing, shelter, food, protection from enemies, even for belonging. This provision is summed up in God's words to his people through Jeremiah: *"For I know well the plans I have in mind for you, says the Lord, plans for your welfare, not for woe! plans to give you a future full of hope…Yes, when you seek me with all your heart, you will find me with you, says the Lord, and I will change your lot."* (Jeremiah 29:11-14)

60

this purpose, they cannot thrive. When we try to attach agendas of our own to God's unconditional love as it operates through our charisms we distort it, sometimes beyond recognition. Avoiding this pitfall, in order to discern your charisms and use them effectively, means you must *turn and meet your fears*. You have to be honest with yourself and face your needs, so that you can find other opportunities to take care of them than through a charism.

On Your Own: The art of releasing control

When we were very young, we were totally dependent upon our parents' or caregivers' love and power for our survival. We had to obtain from them everything we needed, while avoiding what would hurt us. Trying to ensure our survival, we began to *do things* that would got us what we needed and avoided what we didn't want. We learned certain ways of behaving to influence the actions and choices of our parents, and unless we have a very good reason to stop, we tend to carry these strategies with us into adulthood. Even if they did not work very well when we were children, we're inclined to hang onto them because they are familiar and give us the feeling of having some control over what happens to us.

It's important to note that our strategies were based upon our *perceptions* of our caregivers. As anyone who ever idolized a teacher or lay awake in terror of the dark recess under the bed can vouch, our childhood perceptions of the world are not necessarily true or objective. Those of us who are parents know that much of what we do for our children goes right past them, how much they take as their due.

Children are notoriously self-centered. Most of us were fairly oblivious to our parents' struggle to raise us and to the sacrifices they made on our behalf. We thought it was right and good that the world revolve around us and our needs. In the exercise that follows, therefore, we are not seeking to judge or blame our parents, but to uncover our own strategies to control life and deal with our fears. Our childhood perceptions of our parents probably have a good deal of ignorance and unreality mixed into them. But even if they are not the whole truth, they are still important because we *thought* they were true and from these perceptions developed our control strategies to deal with the world.

Sherry Weddell, who developed this program, often uses her own experience as an example. In her perception,

Mom was	Dad was
intensely practical	open to imagination
unpredictable	consistent
demanding	easy-going
humorless	with a good sense of humor
active	passive

In order to get what she wanted and avoid what she didn't, she describes her strategy as one of:
- Anticipating their desires and responses
- in order to give them what they wanted before they asked
- by matching, accommodating, or adapting to them.

61

"As long as I thought I was successfully doing this, I felt that life was in control. But if I failed—if I failed to anticipate their desires, or somehow didn't give them what they wanted—I felt I had to leave, if not physically then emotionally!"

When it came to using the charism of Teaching, her attempts to control outcomes by anticipating, matching, and accommodating people's expectations were a recipe for disaster.

> Here I am, trying to read people's minds (and doing it badly) so I can give them what they want before they ask, and basically lying about who I am and what I really think in order to 'protect' the relationship. In a *Called & Gifted* workshop, I could have 100 different people, all with 100 different personalities, 100 different histories, 100 different reasons for coming, aged anywhere from 16 to 80-plus, exploring 24 different charisms. What do you think would happen if I tried to perfectly anticipate and please everyone, all at the same time? It isn't possible. And in fact, until I learned to let go and stop trying to control the outcome when I was teaching, I had a lot of emotional ups and downs with this charism.

How do you go about *releasing* control?[34] The formula, at least, is simple: take note of your normal strategies for trying to control life and other people, and *do the opposite* while using your charism. For Sherry, the process is as follows:

> When I teach, I deliberately remind myself that everyone present comes with different needs and agendas. I can't know what their needs are, and I can't meet them, either. I acknowledge that those who come are really seeking God, not me, and that God must satisfy them. I offer all that I teach to God, and ask that he would add, subtract, transform or mend it for the best. I've done everything I can to prepare; when it's time to teach I let the words come out of my mouth and wait to see what God does. I have to trust that God will teach people what they need through me, even if they find me boring, unclear, or irritating. To successfully use the charisms we have been given, we have to abandon our attempts to control the outcome and risk using our gifts without knowing exactly what will happen or how others will perceive us.

Now it's your turn to try this. Take a few minutes to reflect on the family in which you grew up. What was your experience of the people or person who took care of you between the ages of 5-13? Using words or brief phrases, describe your parents or caregivers as you perceived them then in the space below.

MOM (or caregiver)   **DAD (or caregiver)**

In this primary world of relationships, you developed your own strategies for trying to control life, to obtain a positive result that you desired or to avoid a negative result. As you reflect back on this world, what strategies did you use that seemed to work for you?

---

[34] See the tip on page 26 for a way to apply this approach next time you use this charism.

62

I tried to keep life under control by:

Now consider the charism that you have been exploring. Can you see how the strategies that you developed for controlling life might get in the way of discerning, developing, or using this gift? (How you might get in the way of this charism by trying to use it to get something you need or avoid something you don't want?) Jot down what you can identify.

Finally, what would releasing control look like for you? What specific action or response could you choose that would be the *opposite* of the habitual control responses you have developed over the years? List one or two ideas below.

God has given you your charisms and God can be trusted to see that he accomplishes what he intends through you. As you become more intentional about releasing control while you exercise your charisms, you'll discover better results.

A prayer to claim God's providence

After the Releasing Control exercise, take a moment to place yourself and your control strategies before God.

Lay down your pen. Quiet yourself. Now, hold up your parents or caregivers to God for his forgiveness, healing and blessing. If you have a sense that a specific weakness needs attention, tell God about it. Whatever insights may have emerged when you meditated on your childhood, whatever you or your caregivers have lacked, ask the Lord to supply it.

Now hold your strategy up. See if the Holy Spirit has anything to say to you about it, any insights as to its meaning, perspectives on its limitations, or understanding of its value. Ask him to speak. Listen quietly for several minutes. If nothing comes to you, it's okay. Remain open to insights he may provide in the future.

Lord, make me an instrument of your peace.
Where there is hatred, let me sow love.
Where there is injury, pardon.
Where there is doubt, faith.
Where there is despair, hope.
Where there is darkness, light.
And where there is sadness, joy.

If you are ready, consciously lay your childhood strategies down. Make an act of humility and trust. You may find the following prayer helpful: "Holy One, I can let go of the need to control situations and other people by...(describe your control strategy). I know you will satisfy the needs you have given me. I want to give up this strategy from my past and truly be used by you to bring your love to others."

O Divine Master, grant that I may not
so much seek to be consoled, as to console;
To be understood, as to understand;
To be loved, as to love;
For it is in giving that we receive—
It is in pardoning that we are pardoned;
And it is in dying that we are born to eternal life.

If you are not ready to do this, that's okay, too. Place that before God. Let it rest, and try to let yourself receive the mercy and acceptance Christ shows to all who are afraid.

Finally, ask for the anointing of the Holy Spirit. Give thanks that God has called you to himself, for your gifts, and for the courage he has given you to come this far. Ask for the grace to answer this call. Do this in your own words, or may want to use the Prayer of St. Francis shown.

What we're *really* doing when we let a charism work freely

To use a charism without skimming something off for yourself is to live a moment of faith, offering your service as an act of obedience through which God may enter the situation. It is to open a door so that eternity may enter time; to magnify the Lord, like Mary.

Think about that for a moment. In the middle of all our concerns to know our gifts, to find out why we're here and what God wants, to find our place in the community, to make our mark...*we are being invited to extend the Incarnation, to bear Christ further into the world.* As the great St. Teresa of Avila put it, "Christ has no body now on earth but yours; yours are the only hands with which He can do His work, yours are the only feet with which He can go about the world, yours are the only eyes through which His compassion can shine forth upon a troubled world."

64

But what about…ME?

If we ourselves have these real needs for love, belonging, security and all the rest—but can't use our charisms to meet them—what *are* we supposed to do? This is a compelling question, given the fact that the overwhelming majority of us come to the discernment process in pursuit of happiness!

Exercising charisms selflessly does *not* mean turning a deaf ear to the pleas of our own hearts. In fact, the more you strive to avoid using your charisms to satisfy your own needs, the more clear (and clamorous!) those needs will become. The better you understand them, the more successful you can be at handling them appropriately. Instead of turning a deaf ear, therefore, we must acknowledge them, and then gently make them wait until after we've finished our charism activity, as we would a child tugging our sleeve demanding lunch. This is the ancient idea of "detachment" — the practice of choosing when and how to respond to our personal needs instead of letting them push us around. Demonstrated by Jesus in the desert, at the well in Samaria, at the death of Lazarus and elsewhere, the Church has continually affirmed detachment as the surprising key to personal satisfaction. We are introduced to it liturgically in the Lenten fast; practicing it while using charisms brings it to bear at the very center of our lives.

How can detaching and making our own needs wait actually result in our fulfillment?

First, it gives us time and freedom to make conscious choices. We are notoriously poor at knowing what will truly satisfy us. If you doubt this, look at the fact that you are participating in this program. Why did you come? To gain a sense of direction? To understand yourself better? To get an idea of how you could contribute more effectively in your church, your workplace, your family? At bottom, couldn't you say you came to this program in pursuit of happiness? Yet this can't be the first thing you've ever undertaken to that end. You've undoubtedly in your life worked at a new friendship, sought a new skill, changed careers, started a family, moved, or bought yourself something special. Each of these does bring happiness. *Yet here you are, still seeking.* Wisdom concludes that we don't fully understand what will make us happy; *simply reacting to our felt needs doesn't do it.*

The trouble with letting our needs lead us is that we tend to act in a way that mainly addresses our feelings, not the situation that triggered them. If Dale is frustrated in his job and spends the whole evening browsing the Internet, he may feel more on top of things, but tomorrow he will have to again face his same frustration. Similarly, if Heather is not cherished at home and tries to use her charism of Pastoring to gain appreciation from others by facilitating a Bible study, she may feel less lonely at first. But the more the group succeeds, and the more focused the conversations become on Scripture, the more Heather will feel discarded again. Detachment, which can be seen as the ability to experience pain without having to shut it out with some coping mechanism, allows us time to see what is true and choose what is truly good for ourselves and others. *Detachment is moving from reaction to response.* If Barbara were able to set aside her longing for appreciation and focus on the group, she might be able to see those persistent feelings better, and strike at the root of the problem. Which brings us to the second way detachment helps us reach happiness.

It allows us to make use of the system God has provided to meet all human needs: relationship—the relationships to family, friends, groups, society, and especially to his own Body, the Church and to himself directly. If we just comfort ourselves every time we feel the twinge of a surfacing need, treating the feeling and ignoring the root, we build up an illusion of control and self-containment that isolates us from asking for and receiving the good things we need from each other.

Best of all, detachment—getting out of the way—allows good things to come to us indirectly from using our charisms. Supernatural gifts tend to draw responses from people who are touched by them, or see others touched by them. Detachment allows us to accept recognition, gratitude, friendship, esteem and love when they do come to us, without extorting them. Both we, and those who offer these prizes, remain free.

65

When you use a charism of the Holy Spirit, you are the rubber meeting the road in the mission of the Church. You are helping realize Christ's work of salvation in this time and place. You are bringing the love, healing, forgiveness, justice, and restoration Christ has won for all at Calvary to those still struggling in a broken world. You stand at the axis of human history, collaborating with the Father's work to bring Creation to its ultimate fulfillment and people to their greatest happiness. And in the midst of this, you are becoming who *you* most truly are, stepping into your full human stature.[35] This is no exaggeration! It is the basic teaching of the faith we profess. Each of us has a magnificent destiny offered us that beckons us far, far beyond our human needs and limitations.

Discerning Together: Take stock and move forward

Unless your small group decides to continue gathering on its own to share discernment experiences, this will be your final meeting. It's a good time to review your experience during these past weeks and see where you are now. It's also a good time to think about where you'd like to go from here.

Discussion Questions

Spend a few minutes privately reflecting on the following questions. Then, take the next hour and a half to give each person time to share brief answers. Again, you may listen and give feedback just as you did last time, pointing out what you have observed, or any patterns you have heard the person describe that may help him or her discern.

Briefly remind everyone: What charism have you been exploring and how have you experimented with it?

How has your understanding of this charism changed or evolved over the past four weeks? Has your experience confirmed or made you doubt that you have been given this charism?

---

[35] See the article on Baptism and Confirmation in back (pp. 72-74) for more on the role of Christians in the Church's apostolic mission.

Have you become aware of other charisms that you might have that you were unaware previously? What are they?

Do you already have an idea about what your own personal vocation or call might be, or what it might include? If so, please describe it briefly. Can you see how the charisms you have been given could be used in that vocation?

If you don't know what your vocation or call is, look at your list of charisms from your Inventory results. Can you see areas in which these possible charisms could be used in the world outside the parish? Do you have a personal "burden" or concern in any of these areas? Are there any areas where it looks like your sense of concern and your charisms converge?

Closing prayer

Once you've each had a chance to review your discernment experience and share your perspectives on what your vocation might entail, have the group pair up in twos (or threes if needed) and share any special prayer requests that remain at this time. Spend five to ten minutes praying for each other.

> *"Again I say to you, if two of you agree on earth about anything for which they are to pray, it shall be granted to them by my heavenly Father."*
>
> — *Jesus, Matt.18:19*

To pray for your partner, first ask him or her if there is anything yet holding them back from discerning or exercising charisms. (When it's your turn, if you feel comfortable, this might be a good time to share ways in which you've realized you tend to use your charisms to meet your own needs.) Bow your head, and ask God to bless him or her, to fill the person with the Holy Spirit. Ask God to empower the person to use his charisms, and to discern and live his vocation. Then ask God to respond to whatever needs the person has mentioned. Thank God for the gifts he has already bestowed on this person (be specific, if you can) and end with the sign of the cross.

If you're uncomfortable with one-on-one intercession, we urge you to try it. Being on the receiving end of this kind of prayer can be a highly empowering and energizing experience. However, if you really don't want to pray aloud in your own words for the person you are with, you can use this "Blessing of Any Person" from the *St. Joseph People's Prayer Book*:

> Heavenly Father,
> from all eternity you foreknew and willed
> the existence of this person
> whom you endowed with an immortal soul.
> You had a particular vocation for him/her.
> Bless this Person, granting him/her the graces
> to carry out perfectly the design you have in mind.
> May he/she strive for Christian perfection for your own glory and for his/her eternal happiness with you and the Son
> in the unity of the Holy Spirit. Amen.

When you are finished praying one-on-one, rejoin the group for a final closing prayer. We suggest you extend your prayers for the discernment of individuals who have participated in your group to your whole parish or larger faith community. Each *community* also has a unique mission or vocation, its own special role in establishing God's kingdom on earth in its particular geographic territory. Communities themselves have discernable charisms that empower and point to that mission. Your personal experience with the discernment process can put you in a unique position to help your community grow in awareness and move toward success in fulfilling that mission. Prayer is a great way to start! Please feel free to add thanks for specific blessings God has bestowed on your community[36] and petitions for specific needs your church may have to the following prayer.

---

[36] The parish is the primary faith community for lay people. However, if you have been discerning with a group with a special mission of its own such as a Marriage Encounter or St. Vincent de Paul group— or even with a group of coworkers in a secular business— we encourage you to pray for these communities in a similar way.

A Prayer for Community Discernment

Lord Jesus, you are the life of our community.
You save us and lead us in right paths.
You established the Church to be your body in the world
to carry your work forward and bestow your grace
through the sacraments. Holy One, you are Lord of the Gifts.

Today we ask you to revive and unleash the power
our parish has received so often in the sacraments.
We ask that the charisms you have given to members of our
community would emerge and become visible,
That you help us support and nurture each other as we discern
and exercise our spiritual gifts,
That together with you, we may become a channel of God's mercy and
love for the individuals, the neighborhood, the town, the city, and
the nation in which you have placed us.

When you called, even Lazarus awoke. Call our community, Lord,
and unite us to your loving purposes. Amen.

Final suggestions

Six weeks is obviously not enough time for this process. There are many things you can do to continue, individually or as a group. The most basic is to continue experimenting actively with the charism you have been discerning or another one, and take time on a regular basis to reflect on evidence of the three signs. We have designed the reflections and exercises in this workbook to be used repeatedly with that possibility in mind. The process is always the same.

In addition, you might try reading one of the books recommended for the charism you've been exploring that you will find listed on the Catherine of Siena Institute's website (http://www.siena.org). If you haven't already done so, you may want to buy the *Spiritual Gifts Resource Guide* and explore the Scripture passages and saints listed there for your charism. Or, while you're experimenting and discerning, you may want to focus energy on deepening your prayer life and receiving the sacraments with greater desire, attention and openness. Progress in prayer can have a dramatic effect on the operation of spiritual gifts. Finally, you might want to use this workbook and the reflections provided to check-in with yourself six months or a year from now to see how you have grown and what may have emerged in your life.

Blessed be God in all his gifts!

– Constitution of the Order of Preachers, 1228

Additional Helps

The Seven Sanctifying Gifts: Big sisters to the charisms

In the process of identifying and developing your charisms, don't overlook the seven gifts of the Holy Spirit. They aren't just abstract terms you had to memorize for Confirmation! Not only does understanding them make it easier to distinguish them from your charisms; they are in themselves even more helpful, empowering, and practically beneficial than charisms.

We received both the Seven Gifts and the charisms in Baptism and Confirmation to prepare us for our new life as members of Christ's Body. The charisms, of course, supernaturally empower us to do our part of Christ's work in the world. They give us the power to act effectively in the loving service of others. The Seven Gifts of the Holy Spirit, however, are primarily given to us for our own sakes; they give us the power to overcome the human failings we possess and in fact to exceed even our noblest natural capabilities so that we can truly participate in the life and mission of Christ himself. This is why they are called gifts of "sanctifying grace." They sanctify us—conform us to Christ—so that we can see and act as Jesus would. Take a look:

- ❑ **Wisdom** draws us to divine things and disposes us to appreciate and value them. It moves us to reflect on dogmas of belief, makes dwelling on divine truth a joy, and encourages us to judge all things according to their principles.
- ❑ **Understanding** empowers our minds to grasp revealed truths. It gives us insight into the meaning of what we believe, where faith merely assents to what God has revealed.
- ❑ **Knowledge** allows us to rightly judge the place of created things, especially those that come between God and us.
- ❑ **Counsel** empowers us to choose and act successfully in concrete situations. It builds on understanding of revealed truth and knowledge of the relative value of created things, applying these to life. With Counsel, we can transcend the limited ability of our natural reason to grasp *all* the facets of a situation, without distortion. Counsel super-naturally empowers the virtue of prudence—the ability to see reality clearly and respond swiftly to realize the good.
- ❑ **Fortitude** is inspired courage provided by the Holy Spirit so that we can persevere in the service of God despite all evils and dangers that oppose us, including our own vulnerability to physical suffering, emotional weakness, and fallible thinking. Fortitude gives us resolve and an indomitable spirit, allowing us to take up the most difficult tasks and endure long and trying difficulties.
- ❑ **Piety** gives us the ability to "worship in Spirit and in truth," by instilling in us deep respect and reverence for God the Father, and for our fellow humans as his sons and daughters. It gives us a filial attitude that facilitates worship and prayer, and strengthens our ability to act with justice toward others.
- ❑ **Fear of the Lord** gives us a profound respect for the power and magnificence of God, and makes sin disgusting to us because it offends him. We see how good God is, how wise, how just, how true, how excellent, how beautiful, and as his children and representatives we fear obscuring that glory with our own thoughts, words, and deeds.[37]

---

[37] Based on *CCC* 1286-1305, 1831; *The Catholic Catechism* by John Hardon, SJ, p. 200-205, 518-520.

71

All of these seven gifts are promised to *every* Christian; so it's important to distinguish between the normal Christian experience of a sanctifying gift and that of a charism. Every Christian can expect to experience the sanctifying gift of Wisdom, which makes it delightful to learn and apply God's truth to our lives. *Not* every Christian will receive the remarkable insight and ability to help *others* solve problems and make decisions that marks the charism of Wisdom. Unlike the charisms, each of the Seven Gifts is meant to benefit us directly and personally. But they can help us develop our charisms, because their main effect is to dispose us to the promptings of the Holy Spirit. Pray for them; you're entitled to them by virtue of Baptism and Confirmation, and they truly help us become clearer conduits for our spiritual gifts.

The Dynamic Duo: Baptism and Confirmation

Baptism and Confirmation are extremely important spiritual foundations for our lives as Christians. Both are sacraments: visible signs given to the Church by Christ that actually impart the grace that they signify. Grace is God's gift of his own divine life, a supernatural and completely unearned gift that enables us to reach the eternal, perfect happiness with God for which we were created. God could channel grace to us through completely spiritual and invisible means, but has chosen to make this grace primarily available to human beings though visible signs—well suited to us because we were created as *embodied* spirits.

If you were ever immersed or had water poured or sprinkled over you while a priest, pastor, or other person said, "I baptize you in the name of the Father and of the Son and of the Holy Spirit," congratulations! You have been baptized. Baptism is much more than a rite of passage or even a declaration of personal faith; it is the door into a whole new life. Baptism really does what its symbolizes. When you were baptized, some amazing things happened. All your past sins were completely washed away and you were flooded with grace, which included both the sanctifying gifts and charisms of the Holy Spirit. You also received a spiritual mark on your soul (called the baptismal character) that can never be erased. You were consecrated to Christ and made a member of the continuing Body of Christ on earth, the Church.

Baptism is the essential doorway into the fullness of Christian life. Only those who have been baptized can be confirmed. The sacrament of Confirmation, in which the bishop or a priest anoints and prays over a baptized person to be filled with the Holy Spirit, completes what Baptism begins. Confirmation is especially important in our role as apostles, ones whom Christ sends to be a channel of his love for others. Confirmation conveys yet more of God's grace and strengthens our inner life by filling us with the Holy Spirit. It also marks us with a permanent character[38] that gives us the power to confess the faith publicly and to undertake the work of an apostle – to bring Christ to the world. Confirmation is an essential source of the inward spiritual strength that will enable us to use the charisms we have been given in the most free and fruitful manner possible.

---

[38] From whence comes the idea of a "person of character" whose excellence, virtue and integrity truly stand out.

I've been baptized and confirmed and I haven't noticed any significant difference in my life.

Together, Baptism and Confirmation with the Eucharist[39] are the sacramental foundations of the Christian life. However, the sacraments aren't magic. The experiential impact of the sacraments on our lives depends to a great extent upon the faith and spiritual openness with which we receive them. Our faith does not *cause* the grace that is the gift of God, but does make it possible for us to *receive* the grace offered through each sacrament. If the person receiving the sacrament has obstacles of unconfessed sin, lack of faith, or an absence of focused attention, he or she may not receive the full transforming life of God that is being made available. This difference in spiritual openness means that different people can receive different amounts of grace from the same sacrament.

When baptized and confirmed Christians undergo a spiritual awakening, when they remove impediments to receiving all that God desires to give them and begin to seek grace through the sacraments in a deliberate way, things begin to happen! Both Baptism and Confirmation enable us to claim the moment-by-moment supernatural help we need to live our call as disciples and apostles of Jesus Christ. We may have been baptized and confirmed in the past, but the impact of those sacraments on our present and future will be life-changing when we turn to God and ask him to *revive* the graces of those sacraments in our lives.

I am a baptized Catholic but have never been confirmed. Does it matter?

Yes! You are seeking to be a channel of God's love for others or you wouldn't be trying to discern your charisms. But how can anyone fulfill a supernatural mission without supernatural empowerment? Jesus told his first disciples to wait to receive the Holy Spirit before they engaged in mission. These first Christians received the full outpouring of the Holy Spirit at Pentecost and were transformed into fearless and supernaturally empowered apostles. Just like the first disciples, we need to be filled with the Holy Spirit in order to carry out our mission. Through the sacrament of Confirmation, we receive the full outpouring of the Holy Spirit that was granted to the first disciples at Pentecost. Confirmation is so important in the life of a Christian that it is an obligation to receive it if at all possible.

If you have not been confirmed, contact your pastor or the parish staff member who prepares people for Confirmation. Explain that you have not received the sacrament but would like to be prepared to do so. Prepare to receive the life-changing graces of Confirmation by intense prayer, by learning all you can about the purpose of the sacrament, and by removing any obstacles to full spiritual openness.

What if I've been baptized but am not a Catholic? Can I be confirmed?

Any person who has been baptized is a true Christian. Even though not Catholic, they are in real, if imperfect, communion with the Catholic Church. To be confirmed, however, requires that you be in full communion, since the liturgy of Confirmation

---

[39] Eucharist means "thanksgiving" and refers to the central act of Catholic worship: the Mass. During the Mass, the sacrifice of Christ on our behalf is made present again. The body and blood of Christ are truly present under the appearance of the consecrated bread and wine and are received as spiritual food in Holy Communion. Through the Mass and the Eucharist, the transforming graces of Christ's sacrifice are poured out upon all who receive Communion.

begins with the renewal of one's baptismal promises and a profession of the Catholic faith. Consequently, only by embracing the whole of the Catholic faith can you be confirmed in the Catholic Church. A Christian who chooses to enter into full communion with the Catholic Church receives the sacraments of Confirmation, Penance, and the Eucharist when they do so.

If you are interested in exploring the possibility of becoming Catholic, you are not alone. Nearly 90,000 baptized adults from other Christian traditions entered the Catholic Church in 1998 in the United States. The first step is contacting the pastor or a priest at your local Catholic parish. Most parishes have an RCIA (Rite of Christian Initiation for Adults) program where you will be able to explore the Catholic faith with other non-Catholic adults and through which you can enter the Church if you decide to do so. As part of your exploration, be sure and check out our list of recommended books and web sites.

What if I've never been baptized?

Clearly, God is present in your life, drawing forth a desire to be an instrument of his love for others. But if you seek to grow closer to God by following Jesus, you need to join in prayer, worship, and communion with his Body on earth, the Church. For 2,000 years, baptism has been the essential doorway into new life as a follower of Christ and access to the grace of the other sacraments. For a non-baptized adult, entering RCIA (the Rite of Christian Initiation for Adults) is the normal way to become a Catholic. Every year, over 70,000 American adults are baptized into the Catholic Church. In the same liturgy, these new Christians also receive the sacraments of Confirmation, Penance and the Eucharist. Your first step is to contact your local parish and ask if they have an RCIA program that you could attend. Prayer and study are very important parts of your discernment and the books and web sites listed below could be of great help to you on your journey.

Recommended Books:

What Catholics Believe by Mike Aquilina & Fr. Kris D. Stubna, Our Sunday Visitor

Catechism of the Catholic Church, Revised edition, Our Sunday Visitor

The Spirit of Catholicism by Karl Adam, Franciscan University Press

Catholic and Christian by Alan Schreck, Servant Publications

By What Authority: An Evangelical Discovers Holy Tradition by Mark P. Shea, Our Sunday Visitor

Surprised by Truth: 11 Converts Give the Biblical and Historical Reasons for Becoming Catholic edited by Patrick Madrid, Basilica Press

Great internet resources:

For those considering *becoming Catholic* or for information on Catholicism in general, www.siena.org has links to over 1,000 of the best Catholic web sites in cyberspace. Explore the spiritual, historical, intellectual, cultural, and artistic riches of our 2,000-year Tradition, divided into four easily navigated areas. See the links section at http://www.siena.org/

Key to the Charisms

This is a thumbnail guide to the primary details that distinguish each charism from all the rest, at least when they have been fully developed. You can use it to see what to expect from using a charism, to help design experiments that fully test a charism, and to get ideas about how to expand the area in which you use a charism you think you may have.

If you are just starting to explore a gift, or if it's likely that a charism is just emerging, you may not have experienced all of the specifics listed. We have tried to include the most universal elements of each charism. However, the experience of a particular gift can vary quite widely from one person to another. If you have had experiences that are not listed, it doesn't necessarily mean they are not connected to the charism in question.

For each charism, we note six pieces of information for the bearer of the gift: your passion, your focus, what your inner experience will be like, evidence of actual effectiveness, responses you should eventually receive from others, and an important "detachment discipline." *Passion* is what the charism urges you toward, the heart of what you seek to achieve when you use the gift. *Focus* is what you tend to pay attention to in order to fulfill that passion. Finally, the *detachment discipline* describes what you can do to avoid the main way people tend to misuse the charism to meet their own needs. Also, at the end of each set of characteristics you will find a list of possible alternative gifts with which the charism can be confused—a great resource if it appears you do not have a charism you thought you did. Check the alternatives listed to see if your experience fits a different charism.

Please use this tool with gentleness, never self-condemnation. We want you to be empowered to discern and develop your spiritual gifts and take up your unique and singular call!

Administration: Provides the planning and coordination needed to accomplish good things

- Passion: Making good things happen for the Kingdom of God
- Focus: Creating and sustaining the organizational structures to further God's designs

Makes an already established goal or vision happen
Organizes people, resources, and logistical details efficiently
Delegates portions of larger task to others easily, coordinates the work of others toward the overall goal

Personal Experience
Coordinating complicated tasks or events is my idea of a good time!
I feel particularly energetic and creative when organizing a complex task or mission.
I would rather delegate parts of a large task to others than do it all myself.
I feel particularly close to God and prayerful when I organize.

Objective Results

Complex goals or tasks were efficiently accomplished by a team that I facilitated.

I have sorted out confusing or complex tasks into clear, efficient steps that others helped me implement.

I have delegated important parts of larger tasks to others and we have successfully accomplished the job together.

Response of Others:

Complex or overwhelming tasks become clear, manageable, and enjoyable when I'm coordinating things.

People like working with me because we accomplish our goal without a lot of wasted effort or confusion.

People who work with me know that I appreciate the importance of their contribution.

Detachment Discipline:

Giving order without imposing it: Remember that you are organizing for the sake of the community and its objectives, not trying to control life or other people.

> Possible Alternatives: Leadership, Service, Wisdom

Celibacy: Most fulfilled and spiritually fruitful by remaining unmarried and celibate for the sake of Christ

- **Passion:** Freedom to give oneself entirely to a call of God
- **Focus:** A *positive* call to a fulfilling lifestyle, not simply being unmarried

Freedom <u>for something</u>

Personal Experience

Being single is personally and spiritually very satisfying for me.

I enjoy and love others but don't really want to be in a committed romantic relationship.

I want to be free to commit myself totally to a particular call or vocation.

I identify with the experience of many great Christians who were celibate

Objective Results

I have chosen not to marry or pursue a committed romantic relationship.

Friendship, rather than romance, is the most compelling relationship in my life.

I am engaged in a satisfying work or vocation that would make marriage difficult or impossible.

Feedback of Others:

Others notice I seem truly happy and content as a single person

They recognize my singleness has freed me to be used by God in special ways.

Detachment Discipline:

Nurturing intimate friendships that are not possessive.

> Possible Alternatives: Faith, Voluntary Poverty

Craftsmanship: Inspired artistic or creative works that beautifies and/or orders the physical world

- **Passion:** Creating things of **physical** beauty to bring joy to others and glory to God
- **Focus:** Creativity with material things – paint, clay, wood, food, plants, cloth, etc.

More than being "handy" or "crafty", it's inspired, imaginative, creative, innovative

Personal Experience

Working with my hands to create something lovely is profoundly satisfying.
I love to share the beautiful things I create with others.
I feel close to God when I create. Making something beautiful is one of my best ways to pray.

Objective Results

The things I make are powerful or beautiful works of art.
People ask me to make beautiful things for them.
When I want to reach out to others, I frequently do so by creating something beautiful for them.

Response of Others:

They express great joy, delight, or surprise at the things I create.
People say that I have a special artistic gift. The things I make are inspired, artistic creations.
Some say the beautiful things I create help them pray or encounter God.

Detachment Discipline:

Responding to the inspiration you have to make something beautiful, and then sharing it; not letting the desire to please, or to avoid the rejection of others determine your creative work

> **Possible Alternatives: Hospitality, Service, Giving**

Discernment of Spirits: Accurate perception of divine or demonic presence in certain people, places, or things

- **Passion:** Awareness of spiritual realities that nourish or hinder the freedom of people and the work of the Church
- **Focus:** Spiritual realities behind the visible world

Accurate recognition of a spiritual presence (divine or demonic); never judgment of a person
More than intuition, reading body language or a situation, or normal discomfort in the presence of evil
Some Discerners sense only the divine presence, not the presence of an evil spirit

Personal Experience

I have been surprised on several occasions to recognize a spiritual presence in a person, place, or thing when I didn't expect it.
I am vividly aware of the presence of Christ in the Blessed Sacrament and the presence of God in places of prayer.
I avoid places or things associated with the occult because I experience considerable distress in their presence.
I appreciate the opportunity to submit what I have "picked up" to the discernment of wise leaders in my faith community.

Objective Results

My discernment of spiritual presences affecting particular persons or situations has proven to be remarkably accurate.

It has been corroborated by outside, objective evidence on a number of occasions.

I know that I could be wrong in my discernment but it has usually proved to be correct.

Response of Others:

Other people have told me that I am a loving person who is not critical or judgmental.

Others have said I have been accurate in my discernment of spiritual presences in particular situations

They have told me that my discernment of a spiritual presence has made it possible for healing, freedom, or reconciliation to occur in particular situations.

Detachment Discipline:

Safeguard the reputations and well being of others by not disclosing what you have picked up unless there is an urgent pastoral reason to do so, and then only to those who need to know and will handle the information appropriately. Always bear in mind that you could be wrong.

> **Possible Alternatives: Intercessory Prayer, Prophecy, Wisdom**

Encouragement: Nurtures or fosters others through presence and words of comfort, encouragement, and counsel

- **Passion:** Helping individuals grow closer to God and become fully themselves
- **Focus:** The personal and spiritual growth and destiny of *individuals*

Strengthens, heals, and nurtures through one-on-one encounter, presence and words

Is more than 1) active listening; 2) natural sensitivity to feelings; 3) classically feminine modes of communication

Personal Experience

I feel privileged and blessed when someone shares his or her private life and feelings with me.

I am most alive and energized when talking to someone talk about his/her life.

I sense that God is present when an individual is talking to me about deeply personal matters.

Objective Results

Individuals, even strangers, often talk to me about their concerns and inner lives.

People are helped, strengthened, renewed and healed in remarkable ways when they talk to me.

Individuals grow spiritually and change in remarkable and positive ways as a result of talking to me.

Feedback from Others:

They feel safe telling me about deeply personal things.

Talking to me about difficult issues and struggles helps a great deal.

I have been told by professionals or experienced listeners that I have a gift for listening or counseling.

Detachment Discipline:

Giving encouragement without expecting to receive the same in return. Remember, you're striving to avoid using charisms in order to meet your own needs.

> **Possible Alternatives: Evangelism, Helps, Mercy, Teaching, Wisdom**

78

Evangelism: Share the faith in a way that draws others to become Jesus' disciples and responsible members of his Church

- **Passion:** that every person truly encounter Jesus and his Church and become a disciple
- **Focus:** those *outside the Christian community*

Often less involved in parish life because primary interest is people on the edge of or outside the Christian community.

Personal Experience

I love talking about God and the Church with those who aren't practicing Christians.
I seek out opportunities to share my faith with the unchurched.
I enjoy working with other Christians to share the Christian faith with the unchurched.

Objective Results

When I talk about my experience of God with non-Christians, they usually want to know more.
I have helped a number of people draw closer to Jesus and/or enter or return to the Church.

Feedback from Others:

People tell me that the Christian faith seems attractive or compelling when I share my own experience of following Christ.
They find my joy in sharing my faith with non-Christians intriguing or inspiring.
Several people have told me that I've helped them grow closer to God and/or the Church.

Detachment Discipline:

Not being discouraged if those you share your faith with don't respond in obvious ways. Not giving up if other Catholics don't understand why you find sharing your faith with those outside the Church so compelling.

> **Possible Alternatives: Encouragement, Knowledge, Prophecy, Teaching**

Faith: Exceptional trust in the love, power, and provision of God and remarkable freedom to act on this trust

- **Passion:** Aspiring to great or difficult things for God
- **Focus:** Possibilities because we serve a God who makes the impossible happen

More than the virtue of faith, which is normal for all Christians, all of us are called to trust God in hard times
Empowers a person to live a lifestyle of exceptional trust in God

Personal Experience

I seem to thrive and be filled with faith in difficult situations that make other Christians anxious or fearful.
In difficult or impossible situations, I often experience a surge of confidence in God's love and care.
I am attracted to situations that demand that I rely to a remarkable extent upon God's provision.

Objective Results

I have taken risks for the sake of my faith that seem extraordinary to other Christians.
I am so certain of God's love and power to provide that I have successfully undertaken a number of risky endeavors.

Feedback from Others:

They find my vibrant faith in God's goodness and provision inspiring and encouraging.

They are surprised at my unshakeable confidence in God in the midst of uncertainty or crisis.

They find my confidence in God's love and provision extraordinary.

Detachment Discipline:

Trusting God with your eyes wide open. Remember this gift empowers your call—it's not meant to enable you to discard prudence or ignore the legitimate fears and concerns of others.

Possible Alternatives: Giving, Intercession, Leadership, Voluntary Poverty

Giving: Giving with exceptional generosity to those in need

- Passion: Providing the financial and material resources that make good things happen.
- Focus: Financial and material needs of individuals or groups that hinder God's purposes.

Does not require that the giver live a life of voluntary poverty (see Voluntary Poverty)

Giver may have the ability to make money for God's purposes, or resources may come to him or her in remarkable ways

Giving may be focused on a particular area by the influence of other charisms, such as Hospitality, Leadership, Helps, etc.

Personal Experience

I find it very satisfying to provide the financial resources that enable good things to happen.

I find it very frustrating when people suffer or important things don't get done for lack of money or resources.

I am very interested in issues of stewardship and would like all Christians to experience the joy of lavish giving.

I don't worry about giving away too much; God will provide what I need.

Objective Results

I give a lot of money or resources to people and organizations in need.

I have made choices and given up luxuries to give others what they need.

I have made important things possible for individuals or groups by making sizable donations.

I give away a larger percentage of my income than most Christians around me.

Good things move forward in significant ways when I get involved in supporting them financially.

Feedback From Others:

Other people are often surprised at the amount of money I give away.

People or groups that I've helped comment on my exceptional generosity.

Detachment Discipline:

Give to help, encourage, or empower, not to control. Try giving with a low profile, even anonymously!

Possible Alternatives: Faith, Voluntary Poverty, Hospitality

Healing: God uses me to cure illness or restore health where healing is unlikely to happen quickly or at all

- **Passion:** That those who are ill may encounter the healing love of Christ and be cured
- **Focus:** People who suffer from physical, emotional, or spiritual illness

Through the charism of healing, God cures those who are sick (partially or totally).
Usually requires direct personal contact with the person who is ill.
The charism of healing is distinct from the broader ministry of healing which does not necessarily involve cure (a hospice nurse with a charism of mercy can have a powerful healing impact on his/her patients even though they still die from their disease).
All charisms can be sources of healing in the broader sense because all charisms make the love of God present and where God's love is present, healing occurs.

Personal Experience

I know that Christ heals today and I strongly desire to be an instrument of his healing for others.
I sometimes experience bodily heat, tingling, or a strong sense of the presence of God when I'm praying/caring for someone who is ill.

Objective Results

People who are ill often get well with remarkable speed when I pray and/or care for them.
People have been healed through my prayers/care for whom healing would not ordinarily be expected.
I have seen scientifically verifiable healing occur when I pray or care for people who are ill.

Feedback from Others:

My prayers and/or care has been a source of real, unexpected healing for them.
People who are ill often seek me out personally for pray or care.
A number of people have brought their sick friends and family to me to be healed.

Detachment Discipline:

Offer healing without seeking reward or even gratitude. Remember it is God who is healing and you are the privileged witness of his love.

> **Possible Alternatives: Encouragement, Mercy, Intercessory Prayer**

Helps: Offering my talents and charisms to enable another person to serve God and people more effectively

- **Passion:** Enabling another's vision or call to happen
- **Focus:** The vision, vocation, or personal potential of another individual

Prefers to work in the background
Personal; needs direct contact with the one who is being helped
Can get discouraged if unable to see that he/she is making a difference in life of the person they are helping

Personal Experience

I am drawn to particular individuals who need my help to make their dreams or vision come true.

It is very satisfying to know that my work is making it possible for someone else to accomplish great things.

I know that my help in the background has made a big difference to the life and achievements of other people.

I feel close to God when I help another person accomplish something that makes a real difference.

Objective Results

I have enabled others to accomplish goals that would not have been possible without my help.

When I get excited about someone's mission or endeavor, I get ideas about what I could do personally to help him or her succeed and offer to take responsibility to do these things.

Leaders are much more effective when I'm around to assist them.

Feedback From Others:

I have been told that I have enabled other people to accomplish things that would not have been possible without my help.

People I work with tell me how important my contribution is even though I stay behind the scenes.

People wrestling with a complex task often ask me for help in critical areas.

Individuals whom I've helped have appreciated my unusually strong personal investment in their success.

Detachment Discipline:

Saying "no" sometimes and taking on only what you can truly complete. Remember you are valuable whether you succeed at helping this person or not.

Possible Alternatives: Encouragement, Mercy, Service, Teaching

Hospitality: Warmly welcoming and caring for those in need of food, shelter, and friendship

- **Passion:** Nurturing others by making a welcoming place for them
- **Focus:** Those who are new or alone and without a place in the community

Hospitality is a powerful charism of community healing

Hospitality can be exercised toward individuals or groups

Personal Experience

I notice newcomers and strangers and enjoy seeking them out and making them feel welcome.

I really enjoy having people over to my home even if I don't know them.

I have a strong sense that I am serving Christ when I welcome someone to my home or community.

I am very frustrated when newcomers are ignored and not welcomed to the community.

Objective Results

I frequently have guests in my home; people feel comfortable just dropping in.

I have played a very active part in the hospitality activities of my family, parish, workplace, or community

I often plan and put on dinners, parties, or other social gatherings that are very successful.

Feedback From Others

People often comment about how warm and inviting my home is.

Others have told me that they appreciated my friendly welcome when they were new.

Others turn to me for help and leadership when its time to put on family, parish, or community gatherings

Detachment Discipline:

Welcoming others without expecting to receive hospitality in return.. Remember, you're striving to avoid using charisms in order to meet your own needs.

Possible Alternatives: Craftsmanship, Service, Giving, Pastoring

Intercessory Prayer: My prayer for others enables God's love and deliverance to reach them in specific, remarkable ways

- **Passion:** That God's will be done and God's love and provision reach those in need
- **Focus:** Offering my prayer as a channel through which God's will is done and God's provision reaches others.

People with a charism of intercessory prayer don't assume that they know what God wants in a particular situation. They try to "listen" before praying and often receive specific guidance as to how to pray for a given situation.

Intercessors don't usually pray for the same thing forever. They often sense when they have done what God has called them to do and are 'finished.'

Intercessory prayer doesn't require direct contact to be effective. Intercessors are often used to bless the lives of people they never meet and who may live thousands of miles away.

Personal Experience

I find it very compelling and energizing to pray for others in need and can intercede for long periods of time.

I have a strong sense that God is using my prayers to really change people's lives and situations.

I frequently receive guidance from the Holy Spirit regarding how to pray for a particular situation.

Objective Results

I often see specific or remarkable answers to my prayers for other people.

Very difficult situations in my church or community have changed for the better after I've prayed.

The situations of others have improved remarkably after I pray for them.

Feedback From Others

People have told me that my prayers for them have made a real difference.

Others often ask me to pray for them when they are facing difficult situations or decisions.

Christian leaders have asked me personally to pray for them or for the needs of the Christian community

Detachment Discipline:

Seeking guidance and direction from God before interceding for a person or situation is very important. Avoid the temptation to try and control situations or people by praying simply for what you want or think should happen.

Possible Alternatives: Faith, Discernment of Spirits, Healing, Prophecy

Knowledge: Empowered study and intellectual activity resulting in new or clearer understanding of God, people, and the universe

- **Passion:** Seeing, understanding, and contemplating what is true
- **Focus:** Asking questions and seeking answers about the true nature of things; Understanding how people and the universe work at the most fundamental levels.

Common expressions of the charism of knowledge: empowered (though possibly informal) study and research, philosophy, metaphysics, theology, mysticism, experimental science, higher mathematics, psychology etc

The charism of knowledge always requires that what we "see" is passed on, in some manner, to others. Christians with this gift are usually given other charism(s) that empower them to pass on the truth that they see, such as Teaching, Leadership, Writing, Encouragement, Administration, etc.

Personal Experience

I find it enormously compelling and satisfying to study and think deeply about ultimate things.

Exploring the world through study usually moves me to prayer because I know I'm contemplating God's handiwork.

The Church's rich intellectual tradition is an important source of spiritual and personal nourishment for me.

I know that I can really make a difference by helping others grasp the important and exciting truths that I have discovered through my intellectual work.

I believe that grappling with ultimate truths is the most important and practical thing a person can do.

Objective Results

When I study a problem or topic, I prefer to focus on the ideas and underlying principles at work behind events and my assessments usually turn out to be accurate

When others are caught up in emotions, events and details, I find myself pointing out connections to big picture realities like human nature, ethics, natural law, Church or Scriptural teaching or other schools of thought.

I have done creative, original, or groundbreaking intellectual work in my field of interest.

Feedback From Others:

Others recognize my knack for analyzing and understanding the principles operating in a situation..

People seek my help when they need to understand or think through complicated ideas or principles.

Others have told me that my intellectual efforts have resulted in new discoveries or clarity in a particular area.

People who are knowledgeable and respected in my field seek out my perspective and insights.

Detachment Discipline:

Keep humility and patience. Pass on your knowledge freely with a spirit of love and service to build people up, not to prove to yourself or others how smart or valuable you are.

Possible Alternatives: Encouragement, Leadership, Teaching, Wisdom

84

Leadership: Sharing a compelling vision with others that draws them to work together
to make the vision a reality

- **Passion:** Changing things for the better through group vision and mission
- **Focus:** Gathering and moving a group into mission by articulating a vision of how we can change things together

Leaders tend to find themselves compelled by a vision of change in a specific area—education, business, empowerment for a certain group, local community involvement, etc.

Those with the charism of Leadership are empowered particularly to advance human dignity, steward Creation, and work toward the realization of God's loving plans for humanity whatever the specific nature of their vision.

Personal Experience

When confronted with a significant problem my first step is usually to look for ways that a group of people can solve it together.

I get restless if I'm not working to accomplish a personal vision. I tend to see potential problems in advance.

I find maintaining the status quo boring; I love coming up with ways people can work together to create new possibilities.

Empowering groups of people to make the world a better place is a very important part of following Christ for me.

Objective Results

When I share a vision about how to change things for the better, other people usually want to work with me to make it happen.

I have led groups that accomplished important goals that have really improved life for others.

I have energized groups that were stagnant or demoralized by suggesting ways in which we could change our situation for the better.

I have started several new groups or organizations.

Feedback From Others:

Others have told me that I am a leader.

People often spontaneously ask me how they can get involved in accomplishing a vision that I have articulated.

People seem to want to follow me and be part of the mission to which I am committed.

Others seek me out because they are attracted to my vision and/or mission.

Detachment Discipline:

Separating others' response to you as a person from their response to the vision you're communicating; distinguishing between collaborators and personal friends; welcoming and encouraging collaboration from people with whom you may never be personally close.

> **Possible Alternatives: Administration, Faith, Pastoring, Teaching, Wisdom**

Mercy: Practical deeds of compassion that comfort those who suffer and help them experience God's love

- **Passion:** Reaching out to those who suffer through practical deeds of compassion that convey God's love and comfort
- **Focus:** Those who suffer or are rejected by society

85

Personal Experience

I find it very rewarding to relate to and help people in practical ways who are poor or suffering.

Serving Christ in the poor and rejected is a very important part of being a Christian for me.

I find it difficult to understand why others ignore or avoid people who suffer.

Talking is not enough when I seek to comfort others; I want to do something for them.

I know that those who suffer are often people of great spiritual depth and I feel privileged to spend time with them.

Objective Results

Through hands-on action, I have made a positive difference in the lives of many in trouble or pain. I've seen those I've served relax and find rest, or smile and show signs their burdens have lightened.

I've spent time with a number of people who are suffering whom I help by doing practical things that bring real relief.

I spend an unusual amount of time with people who are poor, sick, or marginalized because I find it so compelling.

People who have rejected the comfort or assistance of others are often open and responsive to my help.

Feedback From Others:

People in pain or trouble often tell me that I have really helped them, or seem visibly relieved.

Other people are surprised at how rewarding I find it to spend time with people whom others reject.

I have been told by a number of people that I'm exceptionally compassionate toward those who suffer.

Detachment Discipline:

Serve those who suffer freely without expecting a return. The person receiving God's mercy through you may be in too much pain to respond with gratitude.

> **Possible Alternatives: Encouragement, Service, Helps, Giving, Voluntary Poverty**

Missionary: Effectively and joyfully using your talents and charisms in a second culture

- **Passion:** To be a channel of God's love and provision among people of a culture other than my own
- **Focus:** People and communities of other cultures

This charism empowers the use of another charism(s) such as Mercy, Hospitality, Healing, Teaching, Evangelism, Leadership, Writing, Knowledge, etc. across cultural barriers.

You do not need to travel to another country to serve people of another culture

Is more complicated to discern for those who are raised in a multi-cultural home. The test is can I move easily in a culture other than the cultures of my childhood or family?

Personal Experience

I get restless when I have no opportunities to relate to people of different cultures.

It is very energizing and satisfying for me to spend time with people of another culture.

I feel especially close to God when I am relating to people of a different cultural or linguistic background..

Objective Results

I have lived or worked successfully with people of a very different cultural background.

I have adapted to life in a different culture with remarkable ease.

I have several close friends whose native language and/or culture are different than my own.

I seek out opportunities to spend extensive time in other cultures.

86

Feedback From Others

Friends raised in a different culture have told me that they feel closer to me than to other people from my background.

Others have told me that I have a gift for working cross-culturally.

Detachment Discipline:

Accepting the new culture you're drawn to on its own terms without judging it by the standards and assumptions of the culture of your childhood. All human cultures are flawed and in need of the transforming grace of God, which this charism empowers you to help provide. You can do this best if you seek to appreciate the beauty and wisdom of the new culture while acknowledging the ways in which it is broken and in need of redemption.

> **Possible Alternatives: Evangelism, Faith, Voluntary Poverty**

Music: Writing or performing music for the delight of others and the praise of God

- **Passion:** Expressing human experience or celebrating creation or God's majesty with beautiful sound. Creating and/or performing beautiful music as a way to nourish and delight others and to praise God
- **Focus:** Writing, arranging, teaching, or performing music

Personal Experience

I not only delight in making music, I find it to be a profound act of worship, petition, and praise. Music is one of the best ways that I can pray for others.

Making music is central to my life even if it isn't my livelihood.

I have taken steps to perfect my ability to create music because I want do it well.

Objective Results

I often succeed at writing or performing in a way that does justice to the music I envisioned producing.

The music I created for an event established a remarkably fitting atmosphere; it intensified or gave voice to the essence of the experience, opening up the occasion so that people could participate more fully.

People were engaged and moved in accord with the music performed.

Feedback From Others:

Others consider me a gifted musician.

People have told me they were profoundly moved by a piece I produced. When asked, they say they felt joyous, roused, inspired, and even exquisitely pained by what they heard.

People whom I respect ask to hear my music repeatedly.

Detachment Discipline:

Responding to the inspiration you have to create beautiful music, and then sharing it freely. Avoid the temptation to make music primarily out of the desire to please others, or avoid rejection.

> **Possible Alternatives: Prophecy, Writing**

Pastoring: Building Christian community by nurturing the relationships and long-term spiritual growth of a group

- **Passion:** Nurturing the spiritual growth and inter-relationships of the Christian community
- **Focus:** The life and spiritual growth of the *group* rather than the individual; the inner life of the Christian community

Personal Experience

I love to get people together in a small group to share their faith and grow in their understanding and ability to live the Gospel.

I find it frustrating when the groups that I lead get so large that I can't get to know everyone personally.

I am convinced that building Christian community is one of the most important things that I can do because it strengthens, heals, and spiritually nourishes people in a unique and irreplaceable way.

One of the best ways I can serve God and others is make it possible for people to spend time together exploring the faith and sharing their experiences of following Jesus.

Objective Results

I have taken on the "care and feeding" of faith-centered small groups in my church, neighborhood, or workplace.

When I facilitate a small group, relationships between group members are strengthened and we encounter Christ together.

When I bring people together, they grow stronger in their faith and are empowered to serve Christ and others.

Feedback From Others:

People recognize my unusual ability to bring people together and create a fruitful environment for spiritual growth.

Others have told me that participating in a group I led empowered them to grow spiritually.

I am often invited to lead small groups by my Christian community or by individuals who want to explore aspects of the faith.

Detachment Discipline:

Remember you are empowered to build and spiritually nourish the Christian community. Building community must be separated from striving to create a "family" or network of personal friends for yourself. If you feel personally unappreciated, try to distinguish your personal needs from the good of the Christian community.

Possible Alternatives: Hospitality, Leadership, Teaching

Prophecy: Communicating the word or call of God to individuals or groups through inspired words or actions

- **Passion:** That God's people *hear and respond* to God's call *now*
- **Focus:** What is God saying to this individual or group?

Personal Experience

I feel a special affinity or kinship with the Hebrew prophets or with prophetic saints because I share their urgent desire that God's people hear his call and respond from the heart.

I have unexpectedly found myself with an encouraging or challenging message from God for a person or group.

88

I feel a compelling desire that people respond to and live the truths of Scripture or Church teaching that are their rightful heritage.

This prophetic gift has made me very sensitive to my own limitations. I strive to be open to receiving God's word by spending time in prayer and approaching God and others with gentleness and humility.

Objective Results

I do everything I can to awaken people to God's loving call to them now.

Although I often don't understand the significance of the message I received from God for someone else, it usually has a deep personal significance for the person who receives it.

When I pass on what I've received, the word usually sparks worship, repentance, or action.

The words that I have shared have not proven destructive or harmful, but have built up individuals or groups in remarkable or unexpected ways.

Feedback From Others

I have been told others were moved to action, or grew in their faith because I shared a message I was given.

Over time, people whom I respect for their spiritual maturity, wisdom, and knowledge of Church teaching, have come to trust the words that I receive from God and take them seriously.

People have been surprised, even astonished, at the timing and content of what I had to say.

Detachment Discipline:

Practicing discretion in both timing and manner of delivery. Remember, your message is for the building up of people or groups. How and when might they best hear the call of God that you have been given to deliver?

Possible Alternatives: Evangelism, Teaching, Wisdom

Service: Seeing obstacles that keep good things from happening and doing whatever it takes myself to remove them

- **Passion:** Doing whatever it takes to make good things happen
- **Focus:** Unmet organizational needs, potential logistical problems, jobs that need to be taken care of

Personal Experience

I cannot stand the idea that a good project or effort might fail for want of a little elbow grease and common sense.

When I see a problem, obstacle, or unmet need, I just want to get in there and fix it, not talk about it.

I get a lot more pleasure and satisfaction doing things myself than delegating to others

I like to work behind the scenes. I know how important my efforts are to the group's ability to achieve its goals even when others don't fully appreciate what I've done.

Objective Results

I am deeply involved in my church/community because I want good works to succeed and frequently offer to help.

Most projects or efforts I've worked on have been implemented successfully.

I stay energized and stick with a project without having to work closely with the person who is leading it, and without having to help in only one or two particular ways that are special to me. I'm a jack-of-all-trades.

89

Feedback From Others:

People tell me I'm great on a team because I jump in without having to be asked or told what to do
I have been asked by those in leadership roles to get involved in complicated or troubled projects
I've been told I really make a difference—even when my contributions have been "little things"
When something needs to be done, people call me because they know I'm usually ready to help.

Detachment Discipline:

Seek to keep your focus on God as you serve. Accept with serenity that your efforts won't always be met with the gratitude or recognition that they deserve. "Selling" others on the problems that you see before you solve them can help defuse the perception that others might have that you spring into action in order to look good at their expense.

> Possible Alternatives: Administration, Leadership, Helps

Teaching: Enabling others to learn information and skills that help them reach their full spiritual and personal potential

- **Passion:** Changing people's lives by teaching them new information or skills
- **Focus:** How to communicate important information or skill to others

Personal Experience

One of the most vital, fulfilling things I can do is help people acquire the knowledge or skills they need
I tend to zero in on what people need to learn in order to grow.
I enjoy spending time learning new things and figuring out how to help others learn them, too
I find it an especially satisfying and prayerful experience to make the riches of the Christian faith available to other through my teaching.
I love to teach because I have such a vivid sense of how the lives of others are enhanced when they have access to the knowledge and skills that I possess.

Objective Results

I have developed materials or learning opportunities to give people access to new knowledge or skills.
People learn when I teach or from the teaching materials I create. I know this because they have shared their excitement at what they have learned or I have seen them act in more effective ways or do new things.
I often see people suddenly light up with understanding when I explain or demonstrate something.
I am occasionally able to make accessible and compelling subjects that people have been unable to grasp in the past, or to teach people who have struggled with learning previously.

Feedback From Others:

Other people tell me I have helped them learn new concepts or skills that have made a real difference in their lives
People tell me I am able to communicate complicated matters in a way that is clear, compelling, and easy to remember.
People often seek clarity from me about complex subjects they don't fully understand.

Detachment Discipline:

Focus on the material to be conveyed instead of what others think of you. Try to let go of the need to please or be liked and trust that God will teach others through you regardless of how they react to you personally.

> Possible Alternatives: Encouragement, Knowledge, Wisdom, Leadership

Voluntary Poverty: A lifestyle of cheerful, voluntary poverty or simplicity in order to identify with Jesus and the poor

- **Passion:** To be free to identify with Jesus and the poor
- **Focus:** Freedom from material possessions

Personal Experience

I have a sense of solidarity with the poor
One of the most compelling and satisfying ways to live my faith is to live simply, in kinship with Christ and people who have little.
It is easy for me go without many possessions, though I deeply appreciate the inherent goodness of created things and enjoy them.

Objective Results

I dress and eat simply, and go without luxuries and even things others consider essential. I do this cheerfully, with little fanfare.
I am able to use and enjoy created goods deeply without needing or wanting to possess them
Not having things (or struggling to acquire them) frees me to focus on loving and serving others—and I have used that freedom constructively.

Feedback From Others:

Others have told me that they are inspired and touched by my lifestyle.
People who are poor accept me easily because of my simple lifestyle.
Others have told me I have sacrificed a great deal materially in order to follow Jesus or be close to the poor

Detachment Discipline:

Relishing and enjoying good things for their own sake while letting go of the need to personally possess them. Share your sense of freedom with others while resisting the temptation to evaluate their lifestyle by the standards of your own particular call.

> Possible Alternatives: Faith, Giving, Missionary

Wisdom: Insight that comes up with creative solutions to specific problems and enables others to make good decisions

- **Passion:** Helping people by finding inspired practical solutions to personal or group problems
- **Focus:** How do things (people, groups, material things, society, etc.) *really* work? What can we do, practically, to realize the good in this situation?

Personal Experience

I love the experiential wisdom of Christian tradition and enjoy solving practical problems by applying spiritual truths in creative ways—especially in the service of others.

I find it frustrating to be exhorted to achieve some ideal in the absence of the practical tools to make it happen.

I quickly see and get excited about the practical implications of new ideas and information.

I am fascinated by the practical wisdom of others and love to learn all I can about how to really solve problems and make good things happen.

Objective Results

I often apply knowledge (of Christian teaching, human nature, relationships, business or economics, or the created world) in creative ways that change situations for the better.

I have helped others make good decisions that reflected the purpose of God in the midst of uncertainty.

I have come up with innovative or ingenious ideas that made it possible for difficult or seemingly unrealistic goals to be successfully reached.

Feedback From Others:

Others tell me I am very perceptive and talk their problems or decisions over with me in order to take advantage of my insights.

People tell me that I have helped clarify problems or situations that they were struggling with and have helped them see new possibilities or come to a good conclusion.

Individuals or groups consult me about what to do in complex or difficult situations.

Detachment Discipline:

Waiting with humility and with patience for the right moment to speak. Pass on your insights without expectation of reward; build people up rather than prove to yourself or others how smart or valuable you are.

Possible Alternatives: Encouragement, Knowledge, Leadership, Prophecy

Writing: Using words to create works of truth or beauty that reflect human experience and bring glory to God

- **Passion:** Conveying truth and creating beauty through words
- **Focus:** Putting words on paper

A person with this charism has a real sense of delight in the magic and power of words, and a fascination with them individually, just in themselves. They love language, and play with it for fun.

Writing often works in tandem with other charisms, such as Encouragement, Teaching, Knowledge, Wisdom, etc.

Personal Experiences

I usually turn to writing when I need to solve a problem, reach out to someone, explore an idea, or respond to a situation—I like to "get things down on paper" or "write it up."

Writing often feels like prayer or precipitates prayer for me. It is an important source of nourishment for my faith life.

I enjoy the work of wrestling ideas and images onto paper. I feel frustrated and dissatisfied when I'm not working on a piece of writing.

I am often deeply moved by the beauty, wit, and expressiveness of the written word—by the way something is said as much as the truth it conveys.

Objective Results

I sit down and write frequently, and come back again and again even when it's a challenge.

I often feel I succeed in putting what I have conceived into words clearly, effectively, and beautifully.

My written work does what it was designed to: persuade, enlighten, shake up, or expose people to an experience through the imagination alone.

Feedback From Others:

People recognize me as being an unusually effective writer.

People often tell me that they were motivated, encouraged, inspired, healed, renewed or otherwise moved toward the good by what I have written.

People ask me for copies of what I have written, or share it with others.

My community recognizes my ability with words.

Detachment Discipline:

Responding to the inspiration you have to write something beautifully, and then sharing it. Avoid the temptation to allow the desire to please others or avoid rejection to dominate how you exercise the gift.

Possible Alternatives: Encouragement, Evangelism, Teaching, Music, Prophecy

Notes

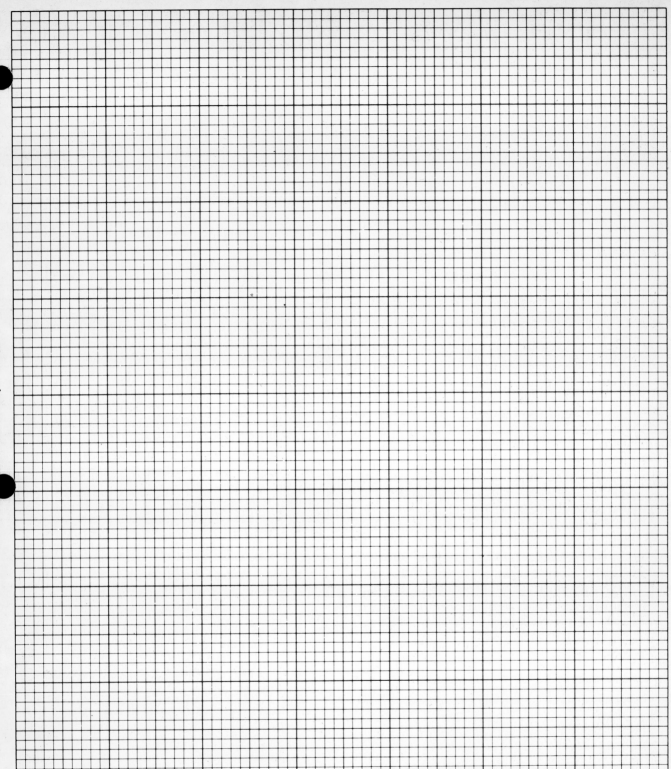

Time to escape circle (vertical axis label)

Angle of board

Fig. 20.4 Diagram showing effect of board angle on time required to escape circle.

tends to follow a definite pattern. Typically, it begins with the crickets approaching each other and touching antennae or with one cricket striking one of its antennae against the other cricket. If neither cricket retreats after this initial encounter, later stages of aggression may involve kicking, producing aggressive sounds (stridulation), grasping the opponent with the forelimbs and mouthparts, and ramming with the head.

The aggressive encounters continue until one of the combatants retreats. Through a series of such encounters among male crickets, a dominance hierarchy becomes established. Periodically the dominant male is challenged by subordinates, and new males entering the area must undergo a similar series of encounters to establish their place in the hierarchy.

Territorialism is the holding and defending of a specific area against other males. This type of behavior is also readily demonstrated with crickets.

Locally collected "wild" field crickets are most suitable for the experiments described here. The domestic ("house") cricket, *Acheta domesticus,* sold commercially by bait houses, is less satisfactory, since the males of this species are less aggressive than field crickets.

Male crickets should be isolated from other males for at least forty-eight hours prior to the experiments. Individual crickets can be isolated in glass jars with screen wire covers. Be sure to provide them with food and water. Oatmeal, cornmeal, or chicken egg layer feed are suitable for cricket food. Small pieces of fruit, such as bananas or apples, are good supplements. A small dish of water to which a ball of absorbent cotton has been added provides a good source of drinking water.

While conducting the following experiments with behavior in crickets, it is important to avoid disturbing the crickets by your presence. Any study in animal behavior requires careful attention to the conditions of the experiment. Keep the terraria dimly lighted during your observations. (Remember that crickets are nocturnal; they tend to be inactive in bright light.) Also avoid touching the table or the terrarium, since crickets are very sensitive to vibration.

Materials needed:

    5- or 10-gallon glass terrarium with screen wire covering

    Male crickets (isolated at least 48 hours prior to experiment)

    Receptive female crickets (isolated from males overnight and provided with containers of moist sand for oviposition)

    Small clay flowerpots or cardboard boxes with holes

    Model paint or fingernail polish

    Toothpicks or small paintbrush for marking crickets

    Vials for transfer of crickets

Procedure

1. Place one male cricket in a dry five- or ten-gallon terrarium. If he sings or calls, describe the call in your notes. If the first male does not produce a call within a few minutes, try another male.

    Time the length of the call with a stopwatch or with the second hand of your watch. Also time the intervals between calls and record them in your notes. How does the cricket produce these sounds? Observe his movement carefully while the sounds are produced.

2. Mark three male crickets with spots of different colored paint (model paint from a hobby shop works well) on the dorsal surface of the prothorax. Assign a letter, A, B, or C, to each male. Place the three marked males in a dry terrarium and observe them for several minutes. Describe in your notes what happens when two males come in contact. How are their antennae involved in the contact? Does the rate, pattern, or intensity of calling change with contact? How are their bodies oriented during contact? You can record such information in your notes with simple diagrams as shown in figure 20.5. Do the males fight?

3. Observe the encounters among the male crickets during the next twenty minutes. Record each fight between the males as a win, loss, or tie for each male. Use a form of shorthand notation, such as A/B or A = B, to indicate the results of each fight. (A/B means A won and B lost, A = B indicates a tie.) Retreat from battle signifies a loss.

    It is also helpful to record the relative intensity of aggressive interactions. Use a numerical scale to indicate the intensity of the conflict.

        1—Retreat immediately after contact
        2—Retreat after aggressive signaling
        3—Retreat after physical contact (fighting)

With this addition your records would look like this:
    1—A/B, 3—B/A, 2—A = B, etc.

After you have completed your observations, answer the following questions.

1. Did the male crickets establish a dominance hierarchy? How is this conclusion supported by your data?

2. If a dominance hierarchy was established, does the frequency and intensity of encounters vary with position in the hierarchy?

3. Does position in the hierarchy seem to be related to size?

4. Do subordinates and dominants differ in the way they approach other crickets?

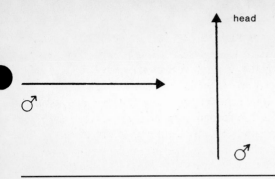

head

♂

♂

Fig. 20.5 Diagram to illustrate aggressive encounter between two crickets.

After you have completed this experiment, exchange your dominant male with that from another group of students. Does the behavior of the subordinate males in your terrarium change?

Remove the two subordinate males from your terrarium and replace them with two males that have been isolated from other crickets for forty-eight hours or more. Are the isolated males more aggressive than the males you observed previously? Does the status of the dominant male in the hierarchy change?

Introduce two juvenile crickets into the terrarium. Do the juveniles challenge the males? Are males aggressive toward the juveniles?

Remove the juveniles and replace them with two receptive females. Does the song of the males change after the introduction of the females? Are the males aggressive toward the females? Does mating occur between one of the males and females? Which male? If mating does occur, can you observe the passage of the spermatophore (sperm packet) to the female? Does mating change the status of the male in the dominance hierarchy?

Territorial Behavior in Crickets

You can also demonstrate territorial behavior in crickets with your simple apparatus. Remove the crickets from the terrarium and place several artificial "burrows" on the bottom of the terrarium. The burrows can consist of small cardboard boxes with holes, small clay flowerpots, or piles of rocks.

Add three to four males to the terrarium and observe how they react to the burrows. If the males take up residence in these burrows and begin to call, gently move two burrows claimed by males closer together. What happens?

Allow the males in your terrarium to establish residence in some of the burrows. Remove any extra burrows and add two new males. What happens? Do the resident males successfully defend their territories against the intruders? How?

Compare your observations with other members or groups in your class. Are your results the same? What differences did you observe? If your results differ somewhat, how might you explain the difference in your observations?

References

Alexander, R. D. 1961. Aggressiveness, territoriality and sexual behavior in field crickets (Orthoptera: Gryllidae). *Behavior* 17:130–223.

Fraenkel, G. S., and Gunn, D. L. 1961. *The orientation of animals*. New York: Dover.

Hainsworth, M.D. 1967. *Experiments in animal behavior*. New York: Houghton Mifflin.

Price, E. O., and Stokes, A. W. 1975. *Animal behavior in the laboratory and field*. San Francisco: W. H. Freeman.

Smith, F. E., and Baylor, E. R. 1953. Color responses in the Cladocera and their ecological significance. *American Naturalist* 87:97–101.

Key Terms

Dominance hierarchy   a social organization of animals established as a result of a series of aggressive encounters ("fights") between competing members of a group. The winning individual exerts his dominance over others in having first preference of food, choice of mates, and pick of nesting locations, etc.

Kinesis   increased movements of an animal in response to some physical stimulus. Direction of movement not oriented either toward or away from the stimulus.

Social behavior   pattern of behavioral responses to other members of the same species.

Taxes   movements of an animal toward or away from a stimulus, such as light, gravity, or humidity.

Territorialism   taking and defending a particular area against other members of the same species except a mate.

Notes and Sketches